'Chinese'
Wilson

THE GREAT PLANT COLLECTORS

'Chinese' Wilson

A life of Ernest H Wilson
1876–1930

Roy W Briggs

Foreword by Roy Lancaster

The Royal Botanic Gardens, Kew

The Royal Botanic Garden, Edinburgh

London: HMSO

© Roy W Briggs 1993

Applications for reproduction should be made to HMSO

ISBN 0 11 250017 X

Cataloguing in Publication Data

A CIP catalogue record for this book
is available from the British Library

Designed by HMSO Graphic Design

Frontispiece: A studio portrait of Ernest H Wilson taken
when he was twenty-three, just before his first trip to China in 1899.

HMSO publications are available from:

HMSO Publications Centre
(Mail, fax and telephone orders only)
PO Box 276, London, SW8 5DT
Telephone orders 071-873 9090
General enquiries 071-873 0011
(queuing system in operation for both numbers)
Fax orders 071-873 8200

HMSO Bookshops
49 High Holborn, London, WC1V 6HB
(counter service only)
071-873 0011   Fax 071-873 8200
258 Broad Street, Birmingham, B1 2HE
021-643 3740   Fax 021-643 6510
Southey House, 33 Wine Street, Bristol, BS1 2BQ
0272-264306   Fax 0272-294515
9–21 Princess Street, Manchester, M60 8AS
061-834 7201   Fax 061-833 0634
16 Arthur Street, Belfast, BT1 4GD
0232 238451   Fax 0232 235401
71 Lothian Road, Edinburgh, EH3 9AZ
031-228 4181   Fax 031-229 2734

HMSO's Accredited Agents
(see Yellow Pages)

and through good booksellers

Printed in the United Kingdom for HMSO
Dd 291789 C30 6/93

For Elspeth, Catherine and Elizabeth

Contents

Maps

Foreword

One of the first plants I met when I embarked on a career in horticulture was a Chinese ragwort, *Senecio tanguticus*. It grew in a walled garden in Moss Bank Park not far from my childhood home in Bolton, Lancashire, and so happy was it in the rich well-cultivated soil there that its creeping rootstock had established a sizeable colony in what was meant to be a mixed herbaceous border. Although in garden terms it was a bit of a 'thug', one had to admire its tenacity, and when in early autumn its large conical plumes of yellow flowers expanded above the deeply cut foliage it was a handsome fellow, to be sure.

Not far away in the same park grew a beautiful Chinese birch, *Betula albosinensis*, quite unlike our native species in its orange-pink bark coated when young with a glaucous bloom. With age the bark darkens and peels away in bold strips and curls. Naturally, these plants intrigued me and later, on checking out their names in a book, I learned that both had originally been introduced by the same man, E H Wilson.

As time passed and my knowledge of plants and their origins increased, Wilson's name cropped up again and again in the stories of plants both common and rare growing in the walled garden and in a large well-stocked rock garden nearby. That was all of forty years ago and since then I have travelled widely and become familiar with a great number of plants introduced from China by Wilson, as well as those of other collectors in eastern Asia. Indeed, several times in the 1980s as a leader of botanical treks and tours I was privileged to follow in Wilson's footsteps in the Chinese provinces of Hubei and Sichuan.

On one such occasion in October 1981, I led a group of fellow plant enthusiasts on a trek to the border regions of Sichuan and Tibet west of the mountain Minya Konka, now known as Gongga Shan. A few hours out of Kangding, known to Wilson as Tachien-lu, we crossed the Zheduo pass at 13,615 ft and there found the yellow poppywort, *Meconopsis integrifolia*, for which the nurseryman Harry James Veitch dispatched Wilson on his second expedition. Time and again on this trek, we encountered plants first collected in the same location by Wilson, which in addition to the poppywort included *Rosa moyesii*, *Hypericum pseudohenryi* and *Viburnum betulifolium*. All these are now represented in my garden from seed collected in 1981, and when in flower are a continuing reminder of Wilson and the plantsman's paradise he explored just over eighty years ago.

Of all those plant hunters who made their reputation in the golden years of Chinese plant introductions earlier this century, none was more productive in garden terms than Wilson. Some collectors may have covered more territory, some undoubtedly collected more dried specimens for scientific study, or more plants and seeds even, but no one successfully introduced more hardy garden ornamentals than he. According to Alfred Rehder, the great taxonomist and dendrologist, who was Wilson's colleague at the Arnold Arboretum and described many of his woody plant introductions, Wilson introduced over 1000 species into cultivation in the West. He further claimed that Wilson's results in that endeavour exceeded those of any other collector. The key word here is results. Like most other collectors before and since, Wilson had his share of frustration and disappointment as a result of seeds and plants being lost in transit or, even worse, perishing in cultivation through ignorance, accident or neglect. Yet, despite the many desirable species (particularly perennials) he introduced that are no longer in cultivation, there remain a great number which continue to give pleasure long after his death.

Walk around any garden worth its salt in North America or Western Europe and I guarantee you will find at least one species which was originally introduced by Wilson, or more likely you will find five or more. It may be a hedge – Wilson introduced *Lonicera nitida* in 1908 – or it may be the flowering cherry in the lawn – Wilson introduced several species of these as well as a number of the Sato Sakura or Japanese cherries. No tree enthusiast's garden would be complete without the paperbark maple, *Acer griseum*, first introduced in 1901, nor would any arboretum proud of the name be without its handkerchief tree, *Davidia involucrata*, first introduced by Wilson at about the same time.

Imagine those miles of borders in parks and urban areas without *Berberis wilsoniae*, *B. verruculosa* and *B. calliantha* together with their numerous hybrids, likewise *Cotoneaster salicifolius*, *Spiraea trichocarpa* and *Viburnum rhytidophyllum*, all Wilson introductions. Think of all those suburban walls and fence lines without *Clematis montana* var. *rubens* and *C. tangutica* var. *obtusiuscula*. When it comes to choice shrubs, Wilson was responsible for a great number that are still recognised by connoisseurs and ordinary gardeners alike as among the very best. They include *Ceratostigma willmottianum*, *Daphne tangutica*, *Deutzia longifolia* var. *veitchii*, *Dipelta floribunda*, *Exochorda giraldii* var. *wilsonii*, *Forsythia ovata*, *Kolkwitzia amabilis*, *Philadelphus purpurascens*, *Rhododendron williamsianum* and *Syringa reflexa*. The list grows ever longer and with it the legend of a man who was regarded even in his own lifetime as a plant hunter extraordinaire.

It was not simply as a plant hunter and botanist that he excelled, however. He was also a highly gifted communicator. Both as a writer of popular accounts of his travels and on plants both wild and cultivated, and as a lecturer and garden guide, he had few equals and was forever in demand. His memory was prodigious. The late Sir Harold Hillier once told me about the day Wilson visited the family firm's home nursery in Winchester some time in the late 1920s. Harold was then a young man and it was his father Edwin who received Wilson at the nursery entrance. Harold's lasting impression of Wilson that day was of a walking encyclopaedia. The very first shrub that Wilson saw on his arrival was one that he had introduced from China and the two Hilliers were treated to a fascinating and animated account of where and when it had been found and how its seeds had been collected and introduced.

Over thirty years later, when I first walked along that famous nursery drive in 1962, the well-stocked borders were still full of trees, shrubs and climbers grown from Wilson's seeds and I can quite appreciate the opportunity it must have given Wilson to enlighten and entertain his hosts. I make no secret of the fact that when I was young, Wilson was one of my heroes. Whilst friends read the everyday minutiae of football stars and popular singers, I found equal satisfaction and pleasure in books about plant explorers, especially Wilson.

His sudden and premature death in 1930 at the age of fifty-four was a tragedy not only to his generation of horticulturists but to those succeeding, for who knows what fresh thrills and adventures he had in store for us, if only in his writings and lectures. Had he lived his full three score years and ten, there can be no doubt that he would have contributed further to the many riches he brought to gardening.

For many years now, the main source of information on Wilson and his travels has been his own books, principal among which are the two-volume *A Naturalist in Western China* (published in America in a single volume under the title *China, Mother of Gardens*) and the two-volume *Plant Hunting*. These are absolutely essential reading for anyone interested in Wilson and the world of the plant hunter. Two accounts of Wilson's life have been published, in 1931[1] and in 1969,[2] but these are now hard to come by. Other information is fragmented,[3] and there has long been a need for a more comprehensive treatment.

This we now have, for Roy Briggs's account extends beyond the story of the dedicated plant hunter to describe his professional activities in Britain and the United States; his interests, including his interest in photography; and his concern about the perils of deforestation. The last-named was a hobby-horse of Wilson's, for despite his zest for collecting he was a conservationist at heart, and like Augustine Henry before him was appalled at man's destruction of his environment.

The author examines Wilson's relationships with his professional colleagues, his friends and with his family, making full use of original documents, including family correspondence previously unpublished and only recently made available. The selection of photographs from Wilson's collection also help provide a clearer insight into Wilson's life and times.

The lives of the pioneer and the explorer have always appealed to the imagination, especially among those unlikely to travel themselves. To armchair travellers, the story of Wilson's exploits as told by Roy Briggs should kindle anew that taste for adventure which makes the humdrum more bearable. For all gardeners meanwhile, armchair or otherwise, it will provide an enjoyable and timely reminder of the debt we owe to this most successful and most English of plant hunters.

Roy Lancaster

Picture credits

The photographs of the places Wilson visited in the Far East and in Australia, India and Africa, and also the photographs of kiwi fruit (p 9), yellow poppywort (p 28) and a Japanese azalea (p 77), were taken by the plant hunter himself, and are reproduced from prints held in the archives of the Royal Botanic Gardens, Kew. Family photographs are reproduced with the permission of Wilson's granddaughter, Mrs Barbara Abbott. Other photographs should be credited as follows: pp 14, 49, 50, 87 and 95 – the Arnold Arboretum, Boston, Massachusetts; pp 8, 9, 12, 19, 44 (both illustrations) and 117, and colour pl. 4 – Roy Briggs; colour pls 2, 3, 14 and 18 – Brinsley Burbidge; colour pls 1, 16 and 21 – C Grey-Wilson; p 62 (regal lily) – Brian Mathew; colour pls 5, 6, 7, 8, 9, 10, 11, 12, 13, 15, 17 and 19 – Photos Horticultural picture library; colour pl. 20 – the Royal Botanic Garden, Edinburgh; pp 12 (Harry James and James Herbert Veitch), 21 and 43 – the Royal Botanic Gardens, Kew.

Acknowledgements

Many people have given help and encouragement during the course of this project and to all of them I would like to express my gratitude. In particular I would like to thank Dorothy and Frank Wilson for their support and encouragement in the early days and up to the present time. Special thanks are due to my good friend Brenda Sullivan, who always liked the story, and who did so much legwork in America on my behalf, and to Sheila Connor of the Arnold Arboretum of Boston, Massachusetts, who made me so welcome when I visited the archives there. A special thanks is also due to Carin Dohlman, whom I have never met, but who gave up so much of her time to sift through the Wilson correspondence at the Arnold Arboretum and forward copies to me in England. My grateful thanks are due to my friends and colleagues who became involved in my 'hobby' at its beginning. In particular I must mention Tim Harpin, who read and reread the draft manuscripts and made so many helpful suggestions. I am grateful to Iris Maynard, whose skill as a librarian did so much to make my research task a pleasant one, and to Dorothy Allen and Linda Davies, who persevered with my appalling handwriting to produce a professional typescript.

I would like to give special thanks to the team of professionals who have brought *'Chinese' Wilson* to a successful conclusion. Here I must acknowledge the help and interest of Valerie Walley of the Royal Botanic Gardens, Kew; Alan Bennell of the Royal Botanic Garden, Edinburgh and that of Philip Glover of HMSO. I am especially grateful for the advice received from my editor, Anne Muffett, who has done so much to polish this story, and to Amanda Hawes, who helped to check the Chinese place names.

My heartfelt thanks go to Barbara Abbott, who gave me unlimited access to her collection of Wilson memorabilia and who, together with her husband Jack, made my family and myself so welcome when we were invited to visit them in New York during the summer of 1989. I must also thank Basil Hart, whose skill maintains the Wilson memorial garden at Chipping Campden, for making me welcome in his home during my numerous visits to inspect Wilson memorabilia.

Lastly I wish to express my sincere appreciation to my wife and daughters, who have endured my obsession with this project and have never complained.

Ernest Wilson, his wife Nellie and their daughter Muriel Primrose in 1906.

Introduction

Ernest H Wilson, immortalised as 'Chinese' Wilson, is famous on many counts. In the course of four trips to central and western China between 1899 and 1911 he discovered an enormous number of plants and trees new to the West, many of which are still in cultivation today. His first journey was in search of the handkerchief tree, *Davidia involucrata*, and on his last he brought back the beautiful regal lily. He was also an explorer, in an area that was then still remote from Western influence, and challenging to the hardiest traveller. Last but not least, he was a writer and botanist, whose works range from gripping accounts of his adventures in the Far East to popular books on gardening, and botanical textbooks.

My interest in him, however, is also a personal one – for Ernest H Wilson was my great-uncle. My maternal grandfather was his brother, and my aunt, Dolly Turland, spent much of her childhood in the company of Wilson's wife and only daughter, who were left with his family in Birmingham while he travelled abroad. On the death of my aunt in 1985, a collection of letters written by Ernest Wilson to his family while on his travels came to light. This sparked off my interest in the famous plant hunter and made me wonder whether more unpublished archive material might be uncovered.

As I read and reread Wilson's books, and began to research the background to his life, I found myself more and more fascinated. Not only had his original journals survived, and many of his letters to his mother and sisters, but also a wealth of photographs taken by him in the field, many of them previously unpublished. Together with the documents – train tickets, annotated maps, travel accreditations – he so scrupulously preserved, they open a window into a world that has vanished forever.

More than fifty years after his death, none of those who knew him well are still alive. Even in life, however, as his friend and biographer Edward Farrington relates (in a book that appeared shortly after Wilson's death), he was difficult to know. Courteous but uncommunicative with strangers, amiable but reserved with casual acquaintances, Wilson was only completely relaxed and at ease with close friends.[1] It is in his writings therefore, both published and unpublished, that we need to search if we are to know anything of his character.

Of course, what remains of the unpublished material is incomplete. The material that has been preserved in the Library at Kew concerning Wilson's links with the famous Veitch family, who sponsored his first two expeditions, is almost certainly only part of the original correspondence[2] and it seems that Wilson's letters to his wife were also destroyed.[3] There is enough, however, to provide tantalising glimpses of the private man behind the public one, and to provide the factual details that a biographer needs. For although the books Wilson himself published about plant hunting are mainly autobiographical, they give little indication of sequence or chronology. His exploits are presented as a series of entertaining cameos, with adventures drawn from different expeditions combined thematically for best effect. He says nothing about his family or his upbringing, and touches only lightly on the physical hardships he encountered on his travels.

The journals, in particular, allow us to fill in many of the gaps. Wilson's pencilled entries set out all the details – time and place, temperature and altitude, botanical notes and so forth – that one would expect from such a careful naturalist. They also include some less objective observations on the places he saw: 'a more hot, fly-infested, stinking hole . . . I have not experienced,' he wrote of one village, 'we all felt better when clear of this filthy pestiferous place.'[4] These journal entries, some of which he published in a series of articles in *Gardeners' Chronicle*,[5] were to be the basis of his best-selling books about plant hunting, but when he revised them for publication in book form, he softened and lightened them. In doing so, he removed much ill humour, to be sure, but he also concealed from the reader much of the mental and physical strain that the journeys imposed. The traveller in the books is fearless and resolute, stoical if not cheerful in the face of adversity. The writer of the journals, however, is often weary and demoralised, aroused to anger by the dirt and squalor he sees around him.

Wilson wrote a great deal while he was travelling. In addition to the journals, he wrote long letters to his sponsors, reporting on his progress and commenting on the landscapes and flora he saw, and also to his mother and sisters in Birmingham.

Wilson's sisters, Florence (left) and May (right), to whom he wrote regularly during his travels.

'CHINESE' WILSON

These last items form an important part of the personal archives to which I have had access, and, like the journals, they make fascinating reading. Here again, a harsher side to his character is sometimes apparent, and we can begin to guess at some of the personal difficulties that lay behind his outwardly glamorous and successful career.

The family was a close one, but life for the Wilsons in England was not easy. Wilson's father, it seems, had a drinking problem, and the family's floristry business was seasonal and at times barely provided a living. Wilson not only wrote to his mother and sisters regularly, he also sent them money, and continued to do so after he was married and had a family of his own. He was the eldest son, and it is clear from his letters that whether or not he was in England and even before his father's death, he saw himself as head of the family, with all the responsibilities that that entailed.

His letters are generally kind and affectionate, but sometimes they chide and scold, and there were some acrimonious exchanges. Occasionally the anxiety he felt about the family's dependence on him erupts with great bitterness: 'for years past you have all regarded me in the light of a lemon to squeeze at will and get all you can,' he wrote to his sister May in 1909, and continued, '. . . Not a single member of the family knows the meaning of the word "thrift" . . . I am glad you have moved into a cheaper house and if only your ideas of economy would lead you to put a few shillings now and again into the Post Office savings Bank you would never regret it.'[6]

Wilson was a photographer as well as a writer. He kept a photographic record of his last two trips to China, as well as his subsequent travels around the world. This picture of a village in western China was taken in 1910.

Part of the difficulty here may have been the fact that relations between Wilson's wife Nellie and his family had never been very good – despite the long periods of time she spent with them when he was away – and she may well have resented their continuing demands on him. They had not approved of the marriage, and he sometimes referred to her rather distantly as 'my wife' in letters to his family. She suffered from ill health all her life and looks tired and strained in nearly all the photographs that have survived.

Most of their early married life was spent apart (Wilson set out on his second trip to China just six months after their wedding), but as none of their letters to each other remain we cannot guess what this meant to them. No doubt a great deal of Wilson's hesitation over his third trip to China, in 1906, which was to last two years, can be attributed to reluctance to part with Nellie and the daughter who had just

Wilson always held his men in high regard and they would often journey many miles to join him on a new expedition. He captioned this photograph 'My Chinese collectors, all faithful and true'.

'CHINESE' WILSON

been born to them, but go he did, and he was to set out for China again, this time for just over one year, in 1910. By that time, they had moved to the United States, so that Wilson could take up an appointment at the Arnold Arboretum in Boston. Nellie, it seems, did not settle happily there,[7] and she must have been glad that both she and their daughter Muriel were able to accompany Wilson on the two trips he made from Boston to Japan, Korea and Taiwan. 'Having them with me makes it much pleasanter and infinitely less lonely for me,' Wilson wrote.[8]

Some of his impatience with his family's demands for money and what he saw as their fecklessness may have arisen out of the tight control he himself had had to learn in order to manage resources on his expeditions. He seems to have been punctilious in this, itemising his expenditure to the last copper coin, as the following extract from his accounts shows:

			Hankow taels
April 15th		Purchase boat	
		$320.00 at ex 72	230.40
"	"	Boat furniture	10.80
"	24th	4 cans Kerosine oil	13.25
"	"	Flag etc ex Chinese Customs	6.12
"	"	Bovril & medicines	11.52
"	"	Refitting boat	10.57
"	"	Wages of crew 23 men	
		advanced	94.86
"	"	Boat's crew, food for –	37.33
"	"	" sundries	19.29
"	"	4 Collectors and Coolies [sic]	
		wages adv[anced]	48.36
"	"	Boat Captain's Wages	
		advanced	8.37
"	"	Miscellaneous expenses	
		Ichang	94.78[9]

It is interesting to see the entries here for payments made to his men. He was a good employer and paid fair wages, for which he demanded absolute loyalty in return. Terms and conditions of employment for servants such as his 'Boy-Cook' were set out in tightly written contracts signed by both parties.[10] The fact that he frequently re-engaged men from previous expeditions, and that they often travelled some distance to rejoin him on a new trip shows that he was seen as a good employer. He had to be tough to get what he wanted, however, and although he once criticised his fellow plant collector Frank Meyer for having 'very little sympathy for the yellow race' and glorying 'in the superiority of the white race'[11] the following excerpt from his journal is revealing:

At 7 a.m. I sent the Lowda [the boat's captain] and others ashore to buy the few things needed and impressed upon them that we were to start at 9 o'clock. None returned till 11 o'clock and it was 10 past twelve ere we unmoored. Bullying and threats availed but little but on threatening the Lowda and taking the names of the absentees they got somewhat alarmed and began to curse each other (and me) roundly. Each blamed somebody else but I know full well that the Lowda and the Head tracker are really the persons to blame. When at last we did start everybody was in a bad temper and the bad language was if possible worse than usual. The two soldiers we had on board looked quite scared amidst the hullabaloo . . . they [then] proceeded to make fast for the night . . . (it was only half past nine) [and] I insisted on moving on. They said there were rapids and what not ahead but I would have none of it and with much grumbling they got underway again . . . This crew of mine are difficult to deal with beyond the ordinary. The bare faced lies they tell the obviousness of which is so transparent that one would fain smile were they not annoyed. In river travelling in this part of the world it is always difficult to know when to drive them and when to let them have their way. Tonight I happened to be right and I shall make much capital of it . . . they think that because it's a foreigner they are working for they can take things easy and by magnifying and inventing difficulties serve their own ends. They have yet to learn that foreigners are not such fools as they think.[12]

This sort of impatience only rarely spills into his published work, however, and it is worth noting that Wilson never boasted about his adventures. Though he was delighted to be known as 'Chinese' Wilson, he had to be coaxed to tell of his adventures in the Far East. He must have been aware of the excitement and admiration his plant hunting adventures aroused, and he must have realised that the heroism he was so reticent about played no small part in his fame, but the description of plant hunting he includes in the book of that name is practical and down-to-earth:

First and foremost it is the work of youth for it takes [a] heavy toll of strength and endurance, patience and enthusiasm. A sound constitution and an eminently sane mind are fundamental requisites. An optimistic temperament and abundance of tact are essential in dealing with the difficulties and delays incident upon travel and the idiosyncrasies of native peoples. The more knowledge the hunter has of plants already in cultivation, of gardening and of botany, the greater the chance of success. Some business acumen, [and the] ability to mingle freely and pleasantly with all sorts and conditions of men are added qualifications of no mean order. But above all else tact and a sound physique are needed.[13]

He might have added 'intelligence, curiosity and a passionate interest in the country concerned'. For when Wilson sailed from Liverpool in 1899 on the first leg of his first expedition to western China, he was not only launching himself on a dazzling career as a plant hunter, he was also at the beginning of what was to be a lifelong fascination with the Far East. Despite the size of the caravan that accompanied him on his travels in China, and despite the fact that he had to rely on interpreters and guides throughout, he seems to have been anything but distanced from the country through which he was journeying. The descriptions in *Plant Hunting* say, are as fresh and immediate as if he were travelling alone, and the books are full of local lore and customs. *A Naturalist in Western China*, for example, contains a chapter on the Chinese materia medica, as well as information on the tribespeople of the border regions and on the Buddhist temples and relics on the sacred mountain Emei Shan. Part of the brief for his fourth Chinese expedition was to report on any interesting commercial enterprises he found, and *A Naturalist in Western China* has a great deal of detailed information on plant products and the methods of cultivation and manufacture they involved. He also included shrewd comments on China's highly unstable political situation.

All this bears witness to an extremely lively and enquiring mind. Always an avid reader, he amassed an enormous library at his home in Boston once his plant hunting days were over, and was particularly interested in books on Chinese history. Another way of maintaining the ties with the country he felt he knew so well was to invest in the railway systems that were starting to develop there. In fact most of his investments were in Chinese concerns, but sadly not all of them were wise; the bonds he purchased in the Canton–Kowloon Railway, for instance, were to become worthless paper long before they realised a profit.

The bare facts of Wilson's life – eight years spent in gruelling conditions in China, with just two of those expeditions resulting in over 65,000 specimens – might seem to make him a forbidding figure. Farrington describes him as someone who did not suffer fools gladly, who could cut an individual and care little for giving offence.[14] Family stories tell of a Victorian paterfamilias who could beat his daughter for minor transgressions and once tried to have her sacked from a job he considered unworthy of her.[15] Yet his response to the world of plants was never less than warm and affectionate. A notable idiosyncrasy was the way he would speak of trees as if they were people. Reporters seeking details of his travels would be surprised to hear him talking of a particular tree as 'this chap I met' or 'that fellow'.

He was always eager to share his delight in the plants and flowers he had made his friends, and it is important to remember that alongside his outstanding contribution to horticultural science is the achievement represented by his popular books, which, more than half a century after his death, continue to give pleasure to plant lovers and armchair explorers alike. He felt that he had derived an immense amount of pleasure from his studies and his explorations of the natural world, and was keen that others should do likewise. 'It is a great pity that botany does not figure as an essential item in the education of everyone,' he wrote:

. . . To be able to recognise and interpret the things around vastly increases the joy of living. It is a truism that the more one knows about plants the more interesting they become and the greater the enjoyment derived from their association. Plants with their beauty of form, of leaf and of flower appeal to all and the history of how, when and from whence they came should add to the pleasure we derive from their presence. Nature is a generous mother and with flowers and leaf has decked the world in loveliness. Love of the beautiful in organic or

inorganic life is the most elevating influence permeating the human family. There are no happier folk than plant lovers and none more generous than those who garden.[16]

Wilson's name is commemorated in the scientific names of numerous species,[17] but there are also other living memorials to him. The Birmingham Botanical Gardens, where he underwent much of his early training, now has a 'Wilson border' entirely planted with his introductions, and in 1984 a memorial garden was planted at Chipping Campden, his birthplace. Here can be seen many of his most famous Chinese plants, including the regal lily, which cost him a broken leg and very nearly his life, the kiwi fruit, and, in pride of place, the handkerchief tree, always a favourite of his, which launched him on his incredible career as 'perhaps the greatest of the plant hunters'.[18]

The entrance to the Ernest Wilson memorial garden at Chipping Campden. This small garden contains many of Wilson's plant introductions from the Far East.

Some of Wilson's introductions were of economic importance. *Actinidia deliciosa*, the 'Chinese gooseberry', formed the basis of the New Zealand kiwi fruit industry.

Chapter One
The Making of a Plant Hunter

Ernest Henry Wilson was born on 15 February 1876 in Chipping Campden, Gloucestershire, the son of Henry Wilson, a railway worker, and his wife Annie, née Curtis. He was baptised at St James's church in Campden, and the Wilson family can be traced back through Campden parish records as far back as 1627. While Ernest was still quite young, the family moved to Monkspath, near Shirley, in Warwickshire. Little is known of them at this time, though there is some evidence to suggest that they were engaged in a florist's business. There were to be six children altogether: Ernest was the eldest, followed by Florence, May, Tom and Frank. The youngest, Dick, was born in 1891.

The school he attended was known as 'Shirley Schools'. The original building has been demolished, but its records have survived,[1] and Ernest Wilson's name can be found in the lists of the pupils who received prizes. Only rarely did he mention his early life in his books, but writing about the horse chestnut in *Aristocrats of the Trees* obviously brought back memories:

With schoolboys it is a great favorite for does it not furnish the seeds used to play the famous game of Conquerors? Among my earliest recollections is that of a grove of trees in an ecclesiastical seminary, and much I used to appreciate a generous gift of nuts from the student

Ernest Wilson was born in this house in Chipping Campden in 1876. While he was still a child, he and his family moved to the outskirts of Birmingham.

priests. How carefully one used to bore a hole through them – a horseshoe nail being a favorite tool – dry them afterward, and test their strength in battles with other boys. Some were clever in hardening them by roasting, but, so far as memory serves, mine always burst when placed in the oven.[2]

From the little house where he lived with his parents and sisters the young schoolboy would have had to make a 4-mile round trip to school each day and no doubt had ample opportunity to explore the countryside around. There are still many ancient trees in this area and maybe his interest in botany had its origins in these early excursions. Certainly the outdoor life must have appealed to him, for when he finally left school, at the age of thirteen, he took up employment as an apprentice gardener for the established nursery firm of Hewitts of Solihull.

He must have taken to the work, for by the age of sixteen he was being recommended to the Birmingham Botanical Gardens for employment as one of their gardeners. He began working there in 1893, and stayed for four years. The hours were long – sometimes he had to work seven days a week and sometimes on Christmas Day – and the most he earned for a week's work in his first year was 19 shillings and fourpence.

The first available photograph of Wilson dates from this period. He is shown aged seventeen or so at the centre of a group of young gardeners amidst the potted palms in one of the stove houses. Already he stands out from the crowd; there is an air of confidence about him, and he looks at ease and gives the impression of a young man enjoying life.

It is not certain where he was living at this time. His family had moved from Shirley and were now living at Acocks Green, some 5 miles from Birmingham city centre. This was certainly too far for daily travel so he probably took digs in the Edgbaston area. The most likely address is 25 Parker Street, the family home of his wife-to-be, Miss Ellen Ganderton.

Wilson was not lacking in ambition or determination. Having completed a long day at the gardens he then took himself off several nights a week to study botany at the Birmingham Technical School. Here, during a rigorous practical and theoretical course, he was able to demonstrate an aptitude for his chosen subject. He gained a 'First Class' in the 'Advanced Stage' examination in June 1896, and further distinguished himself by winning the Queen's Prize for the subject.[3]

In January 1897 Wilson finally left Birmingham behind and took up employment with the Royal Botanic Gardens, Kew. Initially his duties were those of any young gardener there and in his spare time he studied for the Higher Grade examination in horticulture administered by the Royal Horticultural Society. He passed twenty-ninth in the first class, and used the National Scholarship he had won to attend a course of botany lectures at the Royal College of Science in South Kensington, passing part 1 of the 'Honours' in May the following year. In October 1898 Wilson left Kew and took up the study of botany at the Royal College full time. His intention was to gain qualifications to become a teacher of the subject he had

'CHINESE' WILSON

come to love. Hardly had his studies begun, however, when he was presented with a very different career opportunity.

In 1882, Dr Augustine Henry had been appointed medical officer and assistant in the customs service at Yichang, in the south of the province of Hubei, China. The Imperial Maritime Customs had originated in the 1850s, at the time of the Taiping Rebellion. During the ensuing chaos the Chinese customs officials had quit their posts and the consuls of Britain, France and the United States assumed the role of tax collectors to the Chinese government.

The earliest known photograph of Ernest Wilson (centre), taken at the Birmingham Botanical Gardens, Edgbaston, in about 1894. He worked hard here and soon established himself as a young man of great potential.

Henry initially began collecting plants as part of his official duties. Reports on vegetable products had to be regularly compiled as part of the customs service import and export returns. In addition the service was required to produce lists of Chinese drugs. Having a smattering of botany, Henry was requested to take responsibility for much of this work. In his spare time, mainly for his own interest, Henry collected specimens of local flora and dispatched particularly unusual examples to Kew. During this amateur botanising, Henry succeeded in sending to England no fewer than 2500 species, of which some 500 were previously unknown. In his letters to Kew, Henry frequently urged the desirability of sending a collector out to his part of China.

At about the same time, James Veitch & Sons at Chelsea (the 'Royal Exotic Nursery') were also[4] interested in plant specimens from China, and they asked the then Director of the Royal Botanic Gardens at Kew, Sir William Thiselton-Dyer, to nominate a suitable collector. Sir William's recommendation was the promising young student, Ernest Wilson, and it was agreed that for a salary of £100 plus expenses for the first year, Wilson would journey to China and collect for the Veitch firm.

This was the start of Wilson's association with the Veitch family, who were also to sponsor his second expedition to western China. He was hired by the head of the firm, Harry James Veitch, who was later joined in the business by his nephews, James Herbert Veitch and John Gould Veitch. While in China, Wilson corresponded regularly with all three.

Before setting out on an expedition that might last several years, it was necessary for Wilson to be adequately prepared, and arrangements were made for him to train at the Veitch premises at Coombe Wood under the firm's top nurseryman George Harrow, and for him to study Henry's specimens at the Kew Herbarium.

Harry James Veitch (top), head of the firm of James Veitch & Sons, who sponsored Wilson's first two expeditions to China, and James Herbert Veitch (bottom). They kept up a regular correspondence with Wilson during his lengthy travels abroad on their behalf.

Right: The Herbarium and Library of the Royal Botanic Gardens, Kew are situated in a building just outside the main gate. New extensions were added later this century, but the original wing shown here is largely unchanged from Wilson's time.

It is interesting that Wilson was to be paid £100, small recompense for the hardships and dangers likely to be encountered on such a trip. This was the sum that had been paid to the 18th-century plant hunter Francis Masson, who had collected for Kew in South Africa, Madeira, the Caribbean and Canada, and it seems that no one had thought it necessary to increase it.

Arrangements were made for Wilson to travel to China via Boston, Massachusetts, in order that he might visit the Arnold Arboretum at Harvard University, and learn of the latest methods of packing and shipping seeds for the long trips from the Orient.[5] Here he was to meet the Arboretum's Director, Professor Charles Sprague Sargent. It seems that Professor Sargent and the Veitches did not always see eye to eye, however, for in March 1899 John Gould Veitch wrote to Wilson:

Enclosed is a letter from the Foreign Office which should be of great value and also a copy my brother has received this morning from Professor Sargent of Harvard University. Read the letter carefully and ask any questions on any point therein that may appeal to you. You will see that the Professor suggests your going to the North first and next year to the South.

Your instructions are of course to go to the South this year and then to the North and in spite of what the Professor says, we think this plan preferable and would prefer your following it . . .

The Professor is a very dogmatic and strong man but you must not let yourself be too impressed by what he says about collecting dried specimens. On this point however, we all know you will be careful, and understand what we want.[6]

It is clear from this letter that the Veitches felt the need to impress upon Wilson that the expedition was primarily a commercial venture. They had to foot the bill and they were determined that time would not be 'wasted' on purely scientific field work.

The Royal Exotic Nursery was not the only firm of horticulturists with an eye on China. Arthur Kilpin Bulley, founder of the famous Bee's Nursery of Chester, had his own man, George Forrest, in the field and a spirit of competition had developed between the two businesses. Although a plant hunting expedition was an extremely costly enterprise, there were great rewards for those who introduced exciting new plant species.

Wilson himself described the prime object of the expedition in his book *Aristocrats of the Garden*. According to this his instructions from Messrs Veitch read:

The object of the journey is to collect a quantity of seeds of a plant the name of which is known to us. This is the object – do not dissipate time, energy, or money on anything else. In furtherance of this you will first endeavour to visit Dr A Henry at Szemao, Yunnan, and obtain from him precise data as to the habitat of this particular plant and information on the flora of Central China in general.[7]

The particular plant referred to was *Davidia*, a rare flowering tree first made known to science in 1869 by the French missionary and naturalist, Père David, after whom it was named. Known in English as the dove tree or the handkerchief tree, it is famous for the spectacular white bracts it bears during the month of May.

A three-year agreement was signed on 27 March 1899 and Wilson travelled north to Liverpool, stopping over briefly in Birmingham to say farewell to his family and his fiancée, Ellen Ganderton. On 11 April he sailed for Boston aboard one of Cunard's regular steam packets, SS *Pavonia*. She was a small ship and though built only seventeen years previously was already obsolete.[8] Conditions aboard would have been fairly spartan, but no doubt Wilson's employers were concerned about cost and she would have provided one of the cheapest Atlantic crossings at the time.[9]

Unfortunately Wilson tells us nothing of the voyage in any of his books, and his journals for this expedition have not been located. The waters of the Atlantic, however, are not noted for their tranquillity and such a journey was still likely to give the thrill of adventure.

Twelve days after leaving Liverpool, Wilson landed at Boston, where he was to spend five days looking over the collections at the Arnold Arboretum and taking advice from Professor Sargent. He later recalled:

Charles Sprague Sargent, Director of the Arnold Arboretum in Boston, Massachusetts, was considered a great authority on the flora of China. He was also an expert on the procedures for collecting and preserving living plant material.

'CHINESE' WILSON

My first meeting with Sargent took place in the shadow of the large pig-nut hickory on Bussey Road in the Arboretum . . . when I was en route to China. After formal greetings he pulled out his watch and said 'I am busy now, but at 10 o'clock next Thursday I shall be glad to see you. Good morning!' I voted him autocrat of the autocrats, but when our next interview took place I found him the kindliest of the autocrats.[10]

Wilson left Boston for San Francisco on 28 April, travelling by the rail network which connected east and west coasts:

My trip across the continent was delightful; everything was new, strange, and interesting, and the hours of daylight were not long enough to drink my fill from the Pullman windows. When crossing Texas a talkative brakesman told me hair-raising stories of the exploits of the notorious James brothers and so impressive was his language that a thrill goes through me now as I recall it.[11]

On 6 May he sailed from San Francisco, and arrived in the busy port of Hong Kong on 3 June. He had various letters of introduction to officials in the colony, and all the necessary arrangements for his stay on the island had been made in advance of his arrival.

Wilson did not wish to stay long in the crown colony, and he made immediate preparations to travel to Simao, where he was to meet Augustine Henry as instructed. Simao was in the south-west of the Chinese province of Yunnan, near the frontier with Burma. In order to reach it, Wilson had to travel first to the port of Haiphong, in what was then the French protectorate of Tongking, and then go via Hanoi to the Chinese border.

One of the reasons he was eager to leave for the mainland was that there was an outbreak of bubonic plague in Hong Kong. However, this also meant that natives of Hong Kong were not allowed to enter Tongking and he was therefore denied the services of an English-speaking Chinese servant. Having no Chinese or French himself, his route through French Indo-China was likely to prove difficult. To add to his problems, relations between Britain and France had cooled to the point where an Englishman travelling through the French colony was likely to be viewed with deep suspicion and at best regarded as a very unwelcome guest. However, Wilson was not a man easily put off and friends of the Veitch firm living in Hong Kong did as much as they could to assist him in obtaining the necessary provisions and travelling outfit for the venture. So, fully equipped and having obtained a passport that would enable him to travel through mainland China without hindrance,[12] he left Hong Kong for Haiphong on 14 June and arrived five days later.

Wasting little time he left that same evening and travelled by river to Hanoi, arriving the following morning. At his hotel he was lucky enough to meet a Frenchman who spoke a little English and he learned of possible trouble ahead. Plans to build a railway connecting Hanoi with Kunming, the provincial capital (then known as Yunnan Fu), had been met with much opposition from the Chinese and there were rumours of increasing anti-European hostility. The route ahead would be a difficult one. He could travel by small steamer up the Red River as far as the frontier town of Lao Cai. From there, navigation was by native boat to Manhao, but the final journey to meet Henry had to be completed overland by mule and sedan chair.

Wilson left Hanoi on the first available steamer on 24 June and had the good fortune to fall in with a young Frenchman who was taking up an appointment with the Chinese Imperial Maritime Customs at Mengzi. He spoke good English and the two arranged to travel together. On the evening of 25 June the pair arrived at Yen Bai, where transfer was made to a steamer of shallower draught for the journey to Lao Cai.

Here, at Yen Bai, the travellers learned that an attack on foreign residents had occurred at Mengzi and that the customs house and French consulate had been destroyed by fire. When the steamer reached Lao Cai, on 29 June, details of the outrage were confirmed. Some short distance from the river was the station of the Chinese Imperial Maritime Customs at Hok'ou. The officer in charge passed on what information he had and gave a warning that the road between Manhao and Mengzi was unsafe for European travellers. The news was very bad. The customs house had been completely razed by fire. The commissioner, his wife and members of his staff had escaped in their night-clothes pursued by a frenzied mob.

The same day, Wilson received a note from the French Commandant in charge of the district warning him not to proceed further on his journey and in the afternoon he was to hear news of a further outrage in which four men had been brutally murdered while *en route* to Mengzi.

The shallow depths often encountered made some of the Chinese rivers unsuitable for steamers. Wilson relied largely on native craft, an example of which is shown here. Travel up-river in these boats was always thrilling and often dangerous.

Wilson had no option but to settle down and wait for the situation to improve. He registered at the newly built Hotel du Commerce and was its very first guest; he records, that the proprietors, a Frenchman and his English-born wife, did much to make life tolerable for him during his enforced stay. Wilson describes Lao Cai as a small village on the left bank of the Red River, hemmed in by low jungle, tree-clad hills and swamps. By day the heat was intense and as it was the rainy season, torrential rain fell every day. It was a very unhealthy spot to be marooned. Across the Red River was a large military barracks containing French Foreign Legion and Annamese troops. An epidemic was raging there and Wilson records that burials of the victims took place nearly every morning and evening. The days of enforced idleness lengthened to weeks and the prospects of continuing the journey to meet Henry looked bleak. In fact Wilson was all set to write to his employers advising the termination of the expedition when things took a turn for the better. On 19 July the commandant sent a note to Wilson informing him that the route to Mengzi was now safe. 'I began enquiries for a servant since it was impossible to travel alone, but the news of the riot had done its work and no-one could be tempted.'[13] But his luck was to hold; a month later he received the following letter:

My Dear Sir,

Before I have wish to do a interpreter with you, because I am very sick cannot to going, at now I have a friend he have learned him English for two years at Hongkong, if you wish to get a interpreter he can do.

Your small servant,
"Limay"[14]

Wilson had no idea who Limay was but it turned out that the bearer of the letter was himself the applicant. Wilson describes him as a Chinese of very unprepossessing appearance who smoked opium and who had been dismissed from the telegraph service for incompetence. Not withstanding this, the man was engaged on the spot and, together with an Annamese who could supposedly cook, Wilson left Lao Cai on 23 August in a small native boat, destination Manhao. This leg of the journey was a very difficult one. The river was in full flood and progress was slow and dangerous. On the third day the party was overtaken by a boat belonging to a Frenchman. Glad to meet another European, he invited Wilson to join him. This, it turned out, was a lucky meeting indeed, for not long after, Wilson's boat came to grief in rapids and having lost both sail and mast was all but overcome. Luckily a transfer of the boat's cargo was possible and three days later, without further mishaps, the combined parties reached Mengzi, on 1 September 1899.

At the rear of the customs house, Wilson saw a grim reminder of the riot two months earlier. Suspended from the branches of a tree were wooden cages containing the heads of five of the rioters, and, he noted, 'Later I met a posse of soldiers bringing in another gruesome looking head.'[15]

Simao still lay seventeen days away and with the help of the commissioner, Wilson speedily organised a caravan of fifteen or sixteen mules and several muleteers. The size of the caravan was necessary because Wilson would be taking several cases of silver to the Chinese officials at Simao and stores for the customs staff as well as his own outfit. The party left on 8 September and finally arrived in Simao on the 24th.

By now the caravan had grown, the original party having been joined *en route* by twenty armed soldiers sent from Pu'er and Simao to act as protection from a gang of highway robbers who had been operating in that area: 'with these twenty picturesquely clad but grotesquely armed soldiers our caravan looked like a small punitive expedition,'[16] Wilson wrote.

He spent several days with Henry, who was able to give much useful advice on the local flora. Henry was also able to provide information on the location of the only known specimen of *Davidia*, though this was perhaps vaguer than Wilson might have wished, for the position of the tree Henry had seen was marked on a map covering some 20,000 sq. miles, drawn on half a page torn from a notebook. The area shown was the sparsely populated region straddling the borders of the provinces of Hubei and Sichuan.

Unlike many of his contemporaries collecting in China, Wilson did not adopt oriental dress. Although this meant he occasionally attracted more attention than he would have liked, he very rarely experienced any difficulties. His companion in this picture is probably Walter Zappey, who accompanied him on his third trip to China.

Wilson left Simao on 16 October to return to Hong Kong, where he arrived on 26 November. Here he was able to report back to his employers in Chelsea and dispatch specimens of interesting plants collected in Yunnan. Here too he was able to catch up on his mail from England, including letters from his employers. James Herbert Veitch wrote to him frequently and often gave him fatherly advice on how to combat the loneliness so often experienced by those who venture into unknown lands: 'do not worry but steadily stick to it day by day . . .'[17] In an earlier letter,[18] he advised him to dress 'as a Chinaman'. Photographs of the plant hunter in the field are few, but none show him in anything but European dress, so the advice seems to have gone unheeded. In this same letter, Veitch, ever mindful of the cost of the expedition, also demanded an account of Wilson's expenses every few months. This clearly annoyed Wilson who, while he complied, reminded him of the original agreement, which called for an annual account, and Veitch dropped the matter.

He now made preparations for an expedition to explore the area that Henry had mapped for him. Yichang was to be his base for the operation, an important treaty port situated on the Yangtze, a thousand miles from its mouth. Leaving Hong Kong, he travelled first to Shanghai and then by river steamer up the Yangtze, arriving at Yichang on 24 February 1900. This was to be his headquarters for the next two years.

Organising such expeditions in China was no easy matter. A large number of men had to be engaged to act as bearers and collectors in order to cope with the volume of equipment needed and the mass of plant materials to be transported. Supplies and equipment had to be obtained and arrangements made for carrying money.

The complex system of coinage in China caused problems for travellers. Seen here, left to right, are examples of string cash, a 10 cent silver coin, copper multiple cash coins and a Chinese silver dollar.

Ensuring that expeditions were supplied with the correct currency was a particularly difficult problem. The coin for the smallest denomination was made of copper or brass, with a square hole in the middle. Known as 'string cash', these

coins were carried on cords strung round the neck, a thousand at a time. However, they were not worth much more than the value of the metal they contained (about one thirty-fifth of a penny in 1900) and as Wilson's men might receive a hundred or so a day as wages, he was obliged to carry large quantities of them with him. As one string of a thousand cash weighed 8lb, it was necessary to employ some men just to carry chests of money, and the expedition was probably burdened with several hundredweight of coins. (Multiple cash pieces were available, but they were minted by individual provinces, and could not be used outside the area where they had been issued.) Silver bullion and silver coin such as the Szechwan dollar (equivalent to 1000 cash) would also be carried on an expedition but this form of currency could cause difficulties too, as there were sometimes arguments over the quality of the silver.

Other essential items were insect powder, quantities of opium pills, Epsom salts, permanganate of potash, and brandy. The opium pills were used as something of a cure-all, for fevers and bouts of dysentery. Wilson sometimes had to play doctor to local dignitaries (see chapter 3) and these supplies could be most useful on such occasions. He also carried quinine sulphate to treat the malarial fevers that were a recurrent problem for European travellers in China at this time.

Wilson's personal equipment included a watch, a compass, a barometer, a pedometer and a pocket altimeter. In addition he carried a gun. This was not for personal protection, but was used to shoot game for the table. His observations were recorded in a pencil-written journal, and he supplemented this information with photographs taken in the field. On the first two expeditions, his camera was a simple one, a small Kodak, probably the vest-pocket type, but for his fourth expedition (see chapter 4) a good photographic record was required, and he took a high quality whole-plate camera with him.

Two sedan chairs also went with the expedition, one for Wilson, and one for his head man or 'Boy'. These chairs were not often used as such, but were carried to indicate Wilson's status. They would give the impression that he was somebody important – someone of the same status as a mandarin, perhaps – and would save him from much interference: 'more useful than a passport' he declared.

On some of his expeditions he carried tents, but as a rule he avoided them, since they seemed to be regarded as a novelty in China and attracted unwanted attention. Generally he used the Chinese inns that were to be found along all the main routes; the vivid descriptions he gives of these show the demands they made on his character and fortitude.

Last but not least there was the equipment for collecting and preserving plant materials, both living and dried specimens. This included the vasculum (a japanned metal box with a hinged lid, for safely transporting plant materials back to his camp), tags and rubber date and numbering stamps for cataloguing the collections, and cardboard, paper, string, glue and ink for mounting and labelling specimens prior to dispatch. Particularly important were the plant presses. Wilson had these specially made up in China. In order to minimise deterioration and the loss of natural colour, it was vital that as much moisture was removed as quickly as possible, but keeping up with the number of specimens collected could be

As well as collecting live plant material, Wilson was also instructed to prepare herbarium specimens. The example shown here is one he made of the leaves, flowers and bracts of *Davidia involucrata*, the handkerchief tree. The notes in the bottom left-hand corner are in Wilson's handwriting.

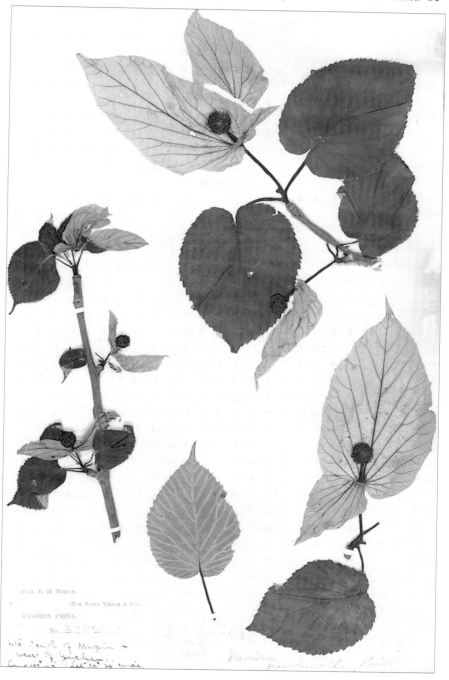

exhausting. 'I worked with nine presses and a thousand "Driers"', Wilson wrote to Sargent in 1907, 'and I assure you changing specimens every night meant work.'[19] Once dried and labelled, the specimens were wrapped in oiled paper for storage and later shipment. Fleshy material unsuitable for pressing was preserved in bottles of what Wilson called 'Chinese spirits', distilled from rice liquor. The type of plant material collected depended on the season. Collecting in the summer months was confined to herbarium material; if seeds were needed, Wilson would have to return in the fruiting season.

These items, together with a hundred and one others, made up Wilson's travelling outfit. The party must indeed have made an impressive sight as it moved about inland China, and it is small wonder that it occasionally attracted more attention than he would have liked. To ease the loneliness that he must surely have felt on these prolonged expeditions, he always took a dog with him. Various dogs appear in photographs of him, and a spaniel is mentioned occasionally in his writings. Such a dog would also have been useful for retrieving game from thick cover.

At Yichang he purchased a native houseboat and engaged a crew. By mid-April his preparations were complete and he was ready to begin the search for the main object of his employment: *Davidia involucrata*, the handkerchief tree.

On 15 April he left Yichang and travelled along the Yangtze to Badong, arriving on 21 April. The journey was a hazardous one (Wilson, characteristically, described it as 'exciting'[20]) because the numerous rapids in that stretch of the river were particularly difficult to negotiate in that season. Twice his boat nearly came to grief on the rocks and there were delays while necessary repairs were made.

At Badong, Wilson and his party were warned of increasing anti-European feelings in the area and the head official did his best to discourage further advance. The man's fears were real enough. In 1898 rioting between anti-Christian and Christian villages had resulted in hundreds of lives being lost and a Roman Catholic priest had been brutally murdered and his body mutilated. Now the same hatred of all things foreign was being whipped up again by reactionary elements.

The empress dowager, feeling that her position was threatened by the spirit of reform brought about by foreign influences in China, had appealed to the people to recreate the old local militia in support of the dynasty. In Manchuria and in the northern provinces of Jilin and Shandong, organised bands of various secret societies were also growing in strength. Among these was the group known to Europeans as the Boxers (the name refers to their martial arts skills), whose banners bore the legend 'By Imperial command exterminate the Christian religion'. Cries of 'Kill the foreign devils' were heard in the streets, and foreigners were in fear for their lives. In June 1900, matters finally came to a head, and the bloody Boxer Rebellion swept through the northern provinces, culminating in the two-month siege of the foreign legation in Peking.

Wilson was certainly not under any illusions about the possible dangers to be risked by continuing his mission. Forty years previously the Taiping Rebellion had raged across China. Hundreds of towns and cities had been reduced to rubble and countless thousands of Chinese had been butchered. However, Wilson reasoned that as he would be operating in fairly remote regions he was unlikely to meet with any hostility. He passed on from Badong on foot following a cross-country road and reached the house where Henry had stayed in 1888 when he had noted the *Davidia* in full flower. Using the Chinese name for *Davidia*, *kung-tung*,[21] they made enquiries and confirmed Henry's observation. A villager acted as guide for the party and they set off in high spirits, their goal soon to be realised. They arrived at a small house, recently built, but where was the *Davidia*? Their guide pointed to a tree stump. The tree they had travelled so far to find had been cut down for timber. Wilson's feelings must have bordered on despair, but all he wrote in his journal was 'I did not sleep during the night of April 25th 1900.'[22]

Back in Yichang, Wilson decided to confine his collecting to western Hubei for the remaining months of that year. He had decided that he would later journey a thousand miles to the west and carry out a search for *Davidia* there, in the area where Père David had first discovered it, in 1869.

In May 1900, when Wilson was exploring to the south-west of Yichang, he came across an interesting climber known locally as *yang-tao*. This vine-like plant bore an interesting fruit that proved to be good eating. Back in Yichang his discovery created quite a stir among the foreign residents, and the fruit was duly christened 'Wilson's Chinese Gooseberry'. This is the plant now grown commercially as the kiwi fruit, *Actinidia deliciosa*.

The treaty port of Yichang was often used by Wilson as his base during collecting trips in Hubei province. Here there was a large European community, and in front of the little native craft can be seen the British gunboat HMS *Teal*.

However, on 19 May, while collecting in the countryside some five days' march south-west of Yichang, Wilson suddenly stumbled across a *Davidia* in full flower. With its large snow-white bracts fluttering in the wind, it must have made a dramatic sight. This tree would always be a particular favourite of Wilson's. He later declared that it was 'the most interesting and most beautiful of the trees which grow in the North temperate regions' and described how when the flowers are 'stirred by the slightest breeze they resemble huge butterflies or small doves hovering amongst the trees.'[23]

While collecting in this region, Wilson later came across two other specimens and then, further afield, eight more. All the trees fruited freely and in November he was able to gather up seed in quantity to ship back to England.[24] It is interesting that although he later came across many other examples of *Davidia* in his travels in China, he never again saw it fruiting as abundantly as he did in 1900.

Back in England, the firm of Veitch were becoming increasingly anxious for the safety of their employee. News of the Chinese rebellion filled the newspapers daily and in October James Veitch wrote to Wilson urging him not to run unnecessary risks and to return home if he could no longer operate there without being in personal danger. However, by the time Wilson received this letter the situation had already improved. The seige at Peking had been broken and the ringleaders of the uprising summarily executed.

The principal objective of the expedition having been achieved, Wilson could now afford to relax a little and continue his collecting where his fancy took him. However, he was ever mindful of what his employers expected of him. The Veitch nurseries were interested in hardy plants. Varieties of plants that required heating under glass were of much less commercial value. Wilson therefore largely ignored the areas in the immediate vicinity of Yichang and headed into the mountains, where vegetation adapted to cool temperate conditions were to be found. These areas were only remotely populated and communications and accommodation were amongst the poorest that he was to experience in all his years in China. Wilson's luck, however, was to hold during this first expedition and he and his party were to experience no serious mishaps.

By the time he was ready to return home in early 1902 he had succeeded in amassing a herbarium collection of nearly 2600 plants and a seed and bulb collection numbering many hundreds of species. Wilson returned to Shanghai and from there sailed for England, arriving at the end of April nearly three years to the day after he had departed from Liverpool.

Once home, Wilson reported to his employers, who were so pleased with his efforts that they presented him with a gold Benson pocket watch inscribed:
'E H WILSON FROM JAMES H VEITCH 1899–1902 "WELL DONE!"'.

Wilson then went to examine the development of the *Davidia* seedlings at Coombe Wood. He was to be disappointed, for not a single seed had germinated. The 'nuts'[25] had arrived in England in the early spring of 1901 and had been sown in various ways. Wilson describes the methods employed in *Aristocrats of the Garden*: 'Some were soaked in hot water, some in cold, others were filed down – in short, everything that a skilled resourceful propagator could think of was put in operation.'[26] Some of the seeds had been put in stove-houses at various temperatures and some planted outside, totally exposed to the elements. Eventually, however, those in the seedbeds outdoors began to show signs of germination, and after a month or so thousands of these had sprouted whereas scarcely any of the seeds planted indoors ever germinated.

Wilson had also brought with him three or four living plants, which were also planted out at Coombe Wood, but it was one of the seedlings that was the first to flower, in May 1911. A cut branch was exhibited at the Royal Horticultural Society's Temple Show in May 1911 and it was awarded a First Class certificate.

The triumph of the successful germination of *Davidia* in England's climate was to be followed by a bitter disappointment for Wilson. In France Maurice de Vilmorin had received seed of *Davidia* from a Roman Catholic missionary, Père Farges, in 1897, and had successfully raised a specimen at his arboretum at Les Barres the following year. Wilson's employers had in fact known of this soon after his dispatch to China, but had decided to keep the news to themselves for fear of dampening his enthusiasm.

The species which Père David discovered had hairy leaves. When Vilmorin's specimen flowered in May 1906, it was found to differ in having smooth leaves and was given the name *Davidia involucrata* var. *vilmoriniana*. It was the hairy-leaved variety which Wilson brought back from his 1900 expedition: he was to succeed in obtaining fruit of var. *vilmoriniana* in 1903, during his second expedition to China, at Baoxing, then known as Mupin, Père David's original locality.

Having completed his business at Coombe Wood, Wilson returned to his family in Birmingham. After three years in China, experiencing all manner of hardships, he would have some interesting stories to tell. No doubt he would also have brought some amazing gifts from the Orient. Certainly his younger brothers Tom, Frank and Dick expected both from their adventurous brother. A family anecdote tells how the boys waited expectantly for their exotic presents from their elder brother: a jewelled dagger, perhaps, or the dried skin of a poisonous snake, things a schoolboy would delight in. In fact they were bitterly disappointed: 'Ernest came home after being in China for three years and all he brought us was a silk handkerchief,' one of them later recalled. A similar piece of silk brought back by Wilson has survived; although it is a beautiful example of Chinese craftsmanship, it is hardly the sort of thing his brothers would have hoped for.

At his fiancée's home in Edgbaston, Wilson discussed arrangements for their marriage and arranged for the calling of the banns. Although Nellie Ganderton was not the wife that Wilson's family would have preferred – it seems that he had been unofficially engaged to someone they liked better – they were married at the parish church of St George, Edgbaston on 8 June 1902.

'CHINESE' WILSON

Another possible reason for the family's disapproval of Nellie is revealed by the details given on their marriage certificate. Both of them, it seems, falsified their ages, probably to conceal the fact that Nellie was four years older than her husband.[27] Today, such matches would not be a matter for comment, but at the turn of the century such a marriage might have been the cause of idle gossip. The Wilsons may also have been unhappy that Ernest seemed to be marrying beneath him; Nellie's father was a jobbing gardener, whereas the Wilsons ran their own business.

If Nellie Wilson thought that her husband was now about to settle down to a life of quiet domesticity, she was soon to be sadly disappointed. The Veitch firm had been greatly encouraged by the wealth of material received from Wilson's expedition to China, and regardless of any objections Nellie might have had, he signed a new contract to travel to China again in the New Year. Perhaps he saw the future as still rather uncertain and viewed a second expedition as an opportunity to become better known in the world of horticulture. Whatever the reason, in January 1903 he said goodbye to his wife and family and set off for the Far East once more, this time sailing direct to Hong Kong, and then on to Shanghai.

Meconopsis integrifolia, the yellow poppywort, the object of Wilson's second trip to China for the firm of Veitch.

Chapter Two

In Search of the Yellow Poppywort

By 22 March 1903, Wilson's steamer was approaching Shanghai. Once again he had written instructions from his employers to find one particular plant. This time, his travels were to take him to the extreme west of China, as far as the Tibetan border. The plant which he was to secure for cultivation was the yellow poppywort, *Meconopsis integrifolia*.

Once in Shanghai, he re-engaged some of the men who had accompanied him on his first expedition, and set out for Yichang. Here he purchased a boat (named the *Ellena*, after his wife) and completed the remaining preparations for the 800-mile journey.

They left Yichang at 5 a.m. on 24 April. By 7 a.m., they were at the entrance to the spectacular Yichang gorges. In his journal entry for that morning, Wilson describes the cliffs as 'alive with lovely flowers, shrubs and herbs in the wildest profusion. Truly a sight for the Gods' and he later wrote 'All the gorges afford such wild and wondrous scenery that neither pen, pencil, brush, nor camera can adequately portray it.'[1]

At 10.00 the boat reached the customs barrier at Pingshan, where the Chinese primula, *Primula sinensis*, parent of so many of the greenhouse primulas cultivated in the West, had been discovered about ninety years earlier.[2] Once their

papers had been checked, they were allowed to continue: 'About a mile above this picturesque village the river takes a right angle turn,' Wilson wrote, 'At this bend, and near the middle of the river, is a large dangerous rock, designated "Sleeping Pig". Rounding this difficulty, we soon came in view of the "Needle of Heaven", an isolated pillar-shaped peak of limestone, perhaps a thousand feet high'.[3]

By 1 o'clock, the party found themselves opposite a pretty little village nestling amidst fragrant orange groves, and they finally put in for the night 30 miles up-river from Yichang. Up until now, the journey had been very pleasant, but beyond the place where they had stopped lay the infamous Yangtze rapids. The first of these, which they tackled the next day, proved to be fairly easy to cross, and Wilson had time to look at the flora of the country through which they were passing. He noted eighty-four distinct species of plants, belonging to seven genera, of which no fewer than twenty-one, he commented, were of horticultural value.

The next day began with heavy rain, forcing the party to tie up again and wait for the weather to clear. The rain slackened off in the early afternoon and with the aid of an extra thirty trackers the boat was hauled safely over another, more dangerous rapid, which took a full hour to clear. Beyond here, the river was known as the 'river of dregs', a name Wilson regarded as wholly appropriate, since the stream was strewn with huge boulders. At high water this became one of the most treacherous parts of the river to navigate.

On the morning of 27 April they set off at 6 a.m. and encountered the first rapid of the day an hour later. This was the Tung-ling rapid, where a German steamer had sunk in 1900. After safely negotiating this, they had but a few hours of clear water before encountering a trio of rapids known as Hsin Tan. They crossed the first of these in half an hour without incident, but the remaining two were only crossed after a lengthy delay caused by heavy rain.

Strong headwinds prevented an early start the following morning, and they did not enter the Mitsang gorge until 8 o'clock. This impressive gorge was some 2 miles long, and the cliff walls reached over 2000 ft in places. Beyond lay the Yeh-Tan rapid, a dangerous place where many lives had been lost.

There were ten junks ahead of them trying to cross this rapid. Each had to be hauled upstream across the roaring torrent by teams of trackers, and the shouts of the men straining at the ropes combined with the sound of the rushing waters to make a deafening clamour. Three of the junks broke free, and as Wilson watched them smashed to matchwood, he must have feared for the *Ellena*. The rest of the party were trying to propitiate the gods: 'My captain chin-chinned, joss crackers were exploded, a little wine and rice were thrown over the bow, joss sticks were burnt, together with candles and some paper cash – in short, every rite necessary to appease the terrible water-dragon was strictly observed.'[4]

It took a hundred men pulling on three huge bamboo ropes twenty minutes to haul the boat over the rapid and into still water. Immediately after Wilson's boat had reached safety, a small native boat with five men on board attempted to follow.

Opposite left: Typical rocky scenery in the vicinity of the famous Yichang gorges. In places the limestone cliffs are several thousand feet high.

Opposite right: Fishing boats near the city of Yichang. As well as nets, the fishermen used specially trained otters.

It capsized and two of the men were drowned. The remaining three were rescued by the red lifeboats permanently moored at the rapid for such eventualities.

By the afternoon of 30 April the expedition had reached Badong and after ascending another bad rapid they entered the 25-mile-long Wushan gorge. In his journal, Wilson describes the flora as 'interesting' but notes that the gorge was a gloomy affair, with vertical walls as high as any previously encountered and with hardly a tracking path anywhere. By the time they tied up for the night, the Hubei–Sichuan border lay only a few miles away.

The month of May began with a chapter of accidents. After an early start, the party had reached the foot of the Lien-Shui-Che rapid. While attempting to tie up here a line broke and the boat was washed down-river. After some time, the party again managed to reach the foot of the rapid, but while the line was being secured, a small boat attempted to get over inshore of them. Unfortunately, its line broke and it was washed across the *Ellena*'s bow. One of Wilson's men was dragged in and drowned, and the *Ellena* was washed down-river again at a terrific rate and nearly capsized in one of the strong whirlpools below the rapids. With great difficulty the party eventually managed to haul in a rope and with much straining made the foot of the rapid once more. Two of Wilson's men were so badly cut and bruised on legs and shoulders that they were unfit for duty. Others suffered minor cuts and bruises.

The owner of the junk to which the small boat belonged had seen the accident and had sailed away post-haste. Wilson, however, was not prepared to let the matter rest there and he set off after him in a lifeboat and overtook him in two hours. He boarded the junk and questioned its owner, who was evasive. Wilson demanded his customs papers and reported the matter to the magistrate at Wushan.

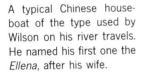

A typical Chinese house-boat of the type used by Wilson on his river travels. He named his first one the *Ellena*, after his wife.

'CHINESE' WILSON

Here he discovered that a tracker's life was reckoned to be worth 6400 cash (about 15 shillings) plus a coffin, should the corpse be recovered. Two months later the owner was found guilty of culpable negligence and fined 100,000 cash (£12). The tracker's family, however, received only the going rate. Presumably the magistrate pocketed the balance. The dead man's brother was one of Wilson's men and Wilson commented: 'Beyond the fact that he was silent and took little or no part in the day's work afterwards, there was nothing to indicate that anything was amiss.'[5]

The expedition now made steady progress up-river. The weather improved and Wilson records having to rest his men frequently as temperatures rose into the upper eighties and nineties. Progress continued to be good, without further mishaps, and some days they made as much as 30 miles. By 21 May the expedition had reached the French naval station situated a few miles below the city of Chongqing. The acting commissioner of customs at Chongqing, W C Haines-Watson, was an old friend,[6] and Wilson must have welcomed the opportunity to take a break from the fatigue and monotony of the river voyage and exchange news of friends and home.

Wilson now pressed on and in five or six days reached Yibin (then known as Suifu), where the Yangtze River (Chang Jiang) becomes the River of Golden Sand (Jinsha Jiang) and joins the Min River. Here Wilson headed north up the Min to Leshan, where he arrived on 19 June.

Leshan (known to Wilson as Kiating) is situated in the west part of the province of Sichuan, where the Min and Dadu rivers converge, 1800 miles from Shanghai. This was to be his base both for the remainder of this year and when he returned to explore the region further in 1904.

River travel in China was often very dangerous on account of rapids, whirlpools and other obstacles. Here the water is strewn with partly submerged boulders, an all too frequent occurrence on the Yangtze.

Wilson describes Leshan as a large and prosperous city containing perhaps 35,000 inhabitants. It was an important trade centre and all goods from down-river were transhipped here to continue their progress by raft. A large silk industry was based here and it had the monopoly of the insect white wax trade.[7] From here it was possible to see the distant mountains of Tibet and the famous sacred mountain Emei Shan, a place of pilgrimage for thousands of Chinese and Tibetans.

In a letter to Sir William Thiselton-Dyer, Wilson describes some of the interesting features of the city:

In the red-sandstone cliffs around here and extending all the way from Chung-King, are numberless caves, square in shape, well excavated and evidently of great age. The Chinese call them 'Mantzu caves' and say they were inhabited by a people called Mantzu more than a thousand years ago. After these people were conquered by the Chinese, they (what few escaped) fled to the mountains north-west of here and their descendents live there to this day. The term 'Mantzu' simply means savage and is applied indiscriminately by Chinese to all aboriginals.[8]

The climate in this region was damp, with little sunshine, though in the summer months the temperature was in excess of 90°F (32°C). Wilson says that November is probably the best month to visit, when three weeks or more of fine weather can be reckoned on.

On 25 June, Wilson set out from Leshan to investigate the countryside in the area of Wa Shan, sister mountain to Emei Shan. It was his intention to climb Wa Shan, which few foreigners had done, and to catalogue the flora he found there.

Kiating (now Leshan) was an important centre of trade for western Sichuan. It was one of the more prosperous cities that Wilson visited, and in this photograph he shows its impressive fortifications.

Wilson's measurements made the altitude of the summit of this mountain to be 11,000 ft above sea-level, some 5150 ft above the surrounding countryside.

On 30 June he arrived at the scattered hamlet he called Ta t'ien-ch'ih, from where he was to begin the ascent. His quarters here were to be the same as those occupied by the noted naturalist and explorer E Colborne Baber, twenty-five years previously. Taking on a local guide, he left the following day at 5.45 a.m. The morning was raw and cold and the going difficult.

During the ascent Wilson made notes on the plant species he observed and on the manner in which one species gave way to another as the altitude increased. At 7000 ft he encountered a dense thicket of bamboo (*Arundinaria nitida*, now called *Sinarundinaria nitida*) which gradually gave way to a mixture of shrubs and herbs, including a few rhododendrons. At 8500 ft he reached a plateau, half a mile across and densely clad with shrubby vegetation and bamboo scrub. Another 1500 ft found him on a narrow ledge and from here to the summit he records that 99 per cent of the ligneous vegetation was made up of rhododendrons. The remaining 1 per cent contained a few conifers, roses and an occasional specimen of *Clematis montana*.

At 10 o'clock the mist cleared sufficiently for him to be able to look over a precipice into an abyss two or three thousand ft deep and hear the roar of a torrent below. Nearing the summit were three vertical cliffs each 40 or 50 ft high, which had to be ascended by wooden ladders set in the rock:

Up these [ladders] I carried my dog, never thinking of the descent. On returning he got frightened, and, though we blind-folded him, he struggled much, and on one occasion his struggles all but upset my balance. I was heartily thankful when solid ground was reached. It requires all one's nerve to mount a ladder, with no balustrade, fixed to a cliff 40 feet vertical and on either side a yawning abyss lost in the clouds.[9]

At 2.30 p.m. it started to rain heavily and continued thus for the whole of the descent. Wilson was very cold and wet when he returned to his inn that evening. He continued to botanise on this mountain for a further three days and succeeded in adding over 200 species to his collection, but the work was excessively hard and they returned to the inn each evening drenched to the skin. On one occasion the career of this intrepid botanist nearly came to a premature conclusion: 'through treading on some loose debris, I was only saved from being precipitated over a steep precipice by the presence of mind of a coolie who happened to be near me at the moment.'[10]

Wilson's party left Ta t'ien-ch'ih on 5 July and took the main road to Hanyuan (then known as Fulin). This was a highway for the salt trade and in his journal Wilson records how he met coolies carrying baskets of salt weighing 2 hundredweight or more on their backs.

They put up for the night at a place he called Yin-Kou:

Our inn was a large one, built in the form of a quadrangle with a small courtyard in the middle, through which the road passed. Doors at either end barred admittance after dark.

The inn was the darkest, dampest and filthiest I had seen. A lightened candle only seemed to make the darkness more intense. How people can live in such dark holes passes my understanding. Nevertheless they all looked healthy and strong, though they are exceedingly filthy even for Chinese.[11]

Some short distance from the inn Wilson noted a specimen of *Davidia involucrata* some 50 ft high. During the day he had seen large specimens of birch, beech, walnut, and *Tetracentron sinense* (a deciduous tree with catkins of yellowish flowers) and a *Magnolia yulan* 80 ft high. 'The day was not long enough to drink in all the charms of the journey,' he comments in his journal, 'and as for being tired, who could be tired amidst such scenery and such flora?'. He was clearly enjoying himself and in very good spirits.

However, the place they arrived at the next day (which Wilson called Huang-mao-chang) was particularly filthy. Its only street was an open sewer, and Wilson commented that 'Its inhabitants are in harmony with the place. They crowded around me as I lunched, and their stench was almost too much for endurance, hungry though I was.'[12]

Many of the Chinese people Wilson encountered had never seen a westerner before, and his arrival in a village was often met with much curiosity.

On 7 July he set off early from his lodgings and began a difficult day's journey through mountainous countryside. After a descent of some 6000 ft he entered the valley of Hanyuan and the town itself some time in the afternoon. He describes Hanyuan as a large and populous place and though he was able to obtain comfortable lodgings he was to experience some minor irritations there.

His spaniel was attacked by local dogs and was only saved – by coolies armed with sticks – with difficulty. He was also bothered by two 'insolent beggars', who demanded money from him and who refused to leave the inn when requested. After sending his card to the local military official with a complaint, a dozen soldiers arrived and the undesirables were roughly ejected. It was unusual for Wilson to be subjected to this kind of annoyance, for his profession entitled him to be treated with as much respect as a mandarin.

During his constant botanising, Wilson had not lost sight of the main aim of his present expedition: securing seed of the yellow poppywort. He hoped to find it in the snowy ranges to the south-west of Leshan, using Kangding, some twelve days' journey away from that town, as a base.

After an arduous and circuitous journey of twenty days, the expedition arrived at Kangding on 14 July. This town, which Wilson calls Tatien-lu or Tachien-lu, was on the borders of China,[13] 18 miles from the Dadu River and twelve days' journey from Chengdu. Wilson described it as a small and filthy place with a mixed population of Tibetans and Chinese. Although the town had no wall, the streets were paved with marble, hardly recognisable under layers of filth. It was a busy trading centre, where wool, musk, hides, gold and medicines were exchanged for coarse brick-tea, tobacco and trinkets. Wilson lodged at a dilapidated Tibetan inn that had served all travellers to the town since the time of Captain W J Gill, who had been the first European to explore the China–Tibet border, in about 1875.[14]

The main road from China to Lhasa was blasted out of the solid rock, 4000 ft above sea-level. Along this road Wilson met men carrying brick tea (right) to Tibet. He measured one man's load at 317lb.

Two days later, on the morning of 16 July, he left Kangding, accompanied this time by another European, a Mr Edgar of the China Inland Mission. As they followed the main road to Lhasa, Wilson comments on the sights and sounds of Tibet: the large lamaseries they passed and their water-powered prayer cylinders, and the prayer 'Om mani padme hum' chanted by the Tibetans as they went about their daily work.

Leaving the main road, they followed a path along a river bank and entered grassy countryside. They passed several farmsteads at an altitude of 10,000 ft and eventually decided to halt at a house at the head of a pass he called the Ya-chia pass to await the baggage coolies, who were lagging behind. While they were waiting, they decided to explore the countryside round about, but half a mile from the house, they were caught in an icy downpour (more like hail than rain, Wilson says) that stung as it struck bare skin. The dog was shivering and howling with the cold, and they rushed back, only to find that the rest of the party had arrived badly affected by the altitude. At that moment they could all have done with a good hot meal but the cook was one of the worst affected. He complained of a pounding headache and heart palpitations and even after a stiff brandy remained unfit for duty.

Many porters had died here in the past, overcome with faintness caused by oxygen deficiency. According to Wilson, the Chinese attributed the symptoms to evil spirits and, since those afflicted assumed that humans were powerless against these, they simply lost hope and died. But for his timely intervention, Wilson claimed, his cook too would have succumbed. Later he was to write that the Ya-chia pass 'enjoys an unenviable reputation . . . and is much dreaded on account of its violent and asphyxiating winds. It is said to be the only pass in the neighbourhood which "stops people's breath".'[15]

The house where they were trying to shelter was dilapidated, with a roof that leaked and a mud floor that quickly turned into a quagmire. An attempt to rig the tent outside had failed on account of the violence of the storm, so it was decided to erect it inside the dwelling. Wilson finally slid under his sodden blankets at about 11 p.m., but there was to be no rest: 'No sooner had I lay down than drip came a spot of rain into my eye, I turned over, and drip came another into my ear. I twisted this way and that way, but there was no escape. Like evil genii these rain-drops pursued me turn which way I would.' His companion suffered the same misery, and sleep was rendered almost impossible. But Wilson's discomfort was to increase:

About 2.00 a.m. I awoke to find that my blanket had slipped over on to the floor; pulling it over me again I disturbed four half drowned chickens whom my thoughtless men had tied to a post alongside my bed. These chickens, resenting the loss of the blanket, tried to follow it and succeeded in nearly blinding me with mud.[16]

At dawn the party arose and breakfasted on ships' biscuits and cheese and Wilson says that he felt none the worse for the night's experience. By 6 o'clock the rain had ceased and at 7 a.m. on 17 July 1903, Wilson set out for the day's excursion on which he hoped to locate *Meconopsis integrifolia*, the plant he had travelled 13,000 miles to find.

At an altitude of 11,000 ft he came across his first specimen, and as he continued his ascent it became more and more abundant. At 12,000 ft and upwards the alpine meadows were covered with the plant, as far as the eye could see.

Many years later, at a lecture given before the Colony Club of New York, Wilson described his triumph in typically modest style: 'On my second trip to China, I went to introduce the Yellow Poppywort . . . having found it rather more easily than I had anticipated, I went out on some information that I had about a red one.'[17]

While looking over the dried specimens of the yellow poppywort at the Kew Herbarium he had come across a reference to a red variety, *Meconopsis punicea*. A label on a dried specimen of this plant read 'Potanin, China borealis, Prov. Szechuan Septentrionale, '85'. Wilson now set out to see if he could discover the habitat of this plant.

Leaving Kangding on 23 July he returned to Leshan by a more direct route via Ya'an, arriving on 4 August. On the 10th he was on the road again. This time his destination was Songpan, a border town situated in the north-west of Sichuan province. Travelling by way of Chengdu, Guan Xian and the Min valley he arrived at Songpan at noon on 27 August:

Sungpan is built in a narrow highly cultivated valley, through which the infant Min winds its circuitous course. The town is walled in by treeless mountains, which rise 1,000 to 2,000 feet above the town. On the west side, Sungpan is backed by a steep mountain, up two sides

The border town of Songpan, looking north from the east gate. This town enjoyed a very mild climate despite its altitude (over 9000 ft), and the standard of living was high.

of which the city wall is carried. The western gate is situated at the top of this mountain, and is exactly 1,000 feet above the river.[18]

After the poverty of the Chinese border country, Songpan was a vision of agricultural prosperity. In spite of the considerable altitude, the town enjoyed a very mild climate. Food was plentiful and cheap and everything from good-quality fresh vegetables to dairy produce was obtainable. Wilson was to visit this area three times during his travels and Songpan was the only town in China he left with any regrets. He later wrote: 'Did the Fates ordain that I should live in Western China I would ask for nothing better than to be domiciled in Sungpan.'[19]

Wilson spent two days investigating the flora of the mountains in the immediate vicinity of the town, but found not a trace of the plant he sought. The people he questioned about the plant were at first reluctant to give information. Eventually, however, he gleaned that a pass known as the Kung-lung pass, some 30 miles north-east of the town, might be a likely place to investigate. On the morning of 30 August, escorted by five mounted soldiers, Wilson left Songpan by the north gate and headed into the mountains. At an altitude of 10,000 ft and 20 miles from Songpan they found lodgings for the night. The house had two large wood fires but no outlet for the smoke save for the door: 'This smoke punished my eyes severely, and at times I thought I should be suffocated. Not so my followers – they did not mind in the least!'[20]

The following day, at 11,500 ft, he saw his first specimen of *Meconopsis integrifolia* and, immediately afterwards, *Meconopsis punicea*, the red poppywort. From 12,000 ft to the head of the Kung-lung pass *Meconopsis punicea* was abundant. The seed capsules were just ripe and a rich harvest of seed was obtained.

To find these two species of *Meconopsis*, Wilson had walked 550 miles in a ten-week journey across the interior of China:

It was harder than anything I had before experienced. I was well-nigh exhausted in body, and almost in spirit, long ere the weary tramp was ended. At Tatien-lu I suffered from mountain sickness and other maladies, and one or two days on the way I had to lay up, but large doses of opium eventually cured me. When I left Kiating, on June 25th, for Tatien-lu I weighed 11st. 4lb., on arrival at Sungpan I was barely 8st. 6 lb. I mention this personal detail merely to show how trying and exhausting the journey proved.[21]

Wilson rarely spoke of his personal experiences in any of his lectures but he was fond of giving his audience a laugh at his expense. In one such lecture he describes an encounter with a friend and colleague at the Royal Horticultural Society show at which *Meconopsis punicea* was exhibited:

I felt rather proud of myself on having made this walk, suffering as I did (or as I thought I suffered) and when this poppy was exhibited in London, I thought I had done something really worthwhile. I happened to be looking at that [Meconopsis punicea] *at the show of the R.H.S. and I turned to a friend of mine, who is now editor of a gardening publication,*

'CHINESE' WILSON

and said 'I walked 700 miles [sic] for that plant'. He looked at me, and said 'Well, Wilson, what a walk!' To rub it in still further, the London Times in describing it, described it as a 'Red rag on a stick'.[22]

During the month of September, Wilson continued his collecting in western Sichuan and then returned to his base at Leshan. He now decided on a short expedition to examine the flora on and around the sacred mountain Emei Shan.

He set out on 13 October 1903, along the road which crossed the fertile plain separating Leshan and the mountain. By nightfall he had reached the little town of Emei Xian, where he took lodgings. The next morning he was able to complete the remaining few miles of the journey and arrived at the foot of the sacred mountain.

This trip so far had been something of an outing, a pleasant change from the hardships endured on recent excursions further north. From here, however, it was to be three days of very hard climbing to the summit, 11,000 ft high. During the first 5000 ft of the ascent, the flora he encountered was subtropical, and he noted some sixty or so different species, mainly evergreen trees, shrubs and ferns. Then the scene suddenly changed:

Emerging ... from a dense thicket onto a narrow ridge 6,100 feet above sea level, a magnificent view presents itself. Above, gigantic limestone cliffs, which ultimately culminate in the Golden Summit; below, valleys and plains filled with a dense cumulus of fleecy clouds, the higher mountain-peaks jutting out like rocky islands in the ocean; to the west, the mighty snow-clad ranges of the Tibetan border, 80 miles distant as the crow flies, stretching north and south as far as the eye can range.[23]

From here on the ascent became more difficult. Ahead lay a formidable stone staircase climbing some 800 ft up the mountain.

After an exhausting climb Wilson was glad to rest at one of the numerous temples dotting the mountainside. It was surrounded on three sides by a grove of silver fir but the fourth side abutted the edge of a terrible precipice. Here he took tea with the priests in charge and heard some of the many myths and legends associated with the sacred mountain. This particular spot, it seemed, was the place where the patron saint of the mountain had first alighted; taking the form of an elephant, he had washed his feet in a pool of water close by.[24]

Proceeding by yet another staircase, Wilson reached a plateau at 9000 ft where he encountered the worst staircase of all. This last took him to within an easy walk of the summit and lodgings for the night in yet another temple.

The flora on the mountain was somewhat disappointing. Apart from the silver firs (*Abies fargesii*), with their striking blue-black cones, he noted thirteen species of rhododendron, but these last, he says, were not as abundant as those he noted on Wa Shan. There were a few bushes of willow, birch and berberis, and *Clematis montana* was fairly abundant, trailing over the shrubs. Despite appalling weather, Wilson remained on the summit for a further four days, adding a few things to his collection. His provisions having now been exhausted, he retreated back down the mountain and returned to Leshan.

In December, Wilson made his way back to Yichang, where he arranged for his collections to be shipped home to England. In April he again journeyed to Leshan, and he spent the months of May and June in the high mountains around Kangding. Conditions in the region, especially in the higher passes, were very harsh; many of his men suffered frost-bite and the whole party was smitten with bouts of snow blindness. In one of his *Gardeners' Chronicle* articles, he gives a graphic account of one such expedition. The party 'consisted of three riding animals, four pack animals, three mounted soldiers, half-dozen coolies, a cook, a missionary friend and myself,' he wrote, 'My travelling companion, Mr Moyes, a member of the China Inland Mission, possessed a thorough knowledge of the Tibetan language, which was of the greatest value.'[25]

After much difficulty in organising transport, they left Kangding by the south gate one 'bright sunny morning', to follow the main road to Batang and Lhasa. Very soon they had left China behind and entered eastern Tibet. The first stopover was at the scattered hamlet of Zheduo. They set out the next day at 6 a.m. and soon reached the snow line, 1000 ft below the head of the Zheduo pass. Wilson describes the scene as 'desolate in the extreme – nothing but snow and bare inhospitable cliffs and crags'. As they climbed, they passed skeletons of yak and horses, some of them only recently dead but already picked clean by vultures.

During the day, two of his men lost their way and the party was delayed at the next halt while they waited for them to turn up. At 8 o'clock the next morning one of

Inhospitable snow-clad mountain ranges in the vicinity of Kangding. Wilson would later describe his travels through this region as the hardest he had ever experienced.

'CHINESE' WILSON

them arrived, in a pitiful state. He had taken shelter the previous night beneath some cairn stones and had spent the dark hours in mortal dread of wild animals, ghosts and demons. A snowstorm and a gale-force wind had further increased the man's discomfort. Of the other man there was still no sign and Wilson sent back some of his soldiers to look for him while the rest of the party pressed on.

The morning of the 11th began with 'damp and mist', Wilson says, but this proved to be a particularly rewarding day. He came across many interesting herbaceous plants, the most striking of which were *Meconopsis henrici, Incarvillea principis* (now called *I. lutea*), *Cypripedium tibeticum* and *Lilium lopophorum*, together with unusual examples of *Primula, Saxifraga, Potentilla, Veronica* and *Fritillaria*. His most surprising find that day was the orchid *Cypripedium guttatum*, which had impressive flowers blotched with dark reddish pink and white. He was also able to secure a pure white form of this.

The following day the soldiers he had sent back returned, bringing in the loads entrusted to the missing man. The man himself limped in a little while later, 'more dead than alive'. He had taken a wrong path at the Zheduo pass and, having spent the intervening time wandering about lost in dreadful weather, was now totally exhausted, and unfit for further duty. Leaving the sick man behind, Wilson and his party continued their journey.

While they were in the process of negotiating the next pass, a storm broke and Wilson and his followers were drenched right through with icy rain. The Tibetans in his party had come prepared for such eventualities: 'clad in thick felts and sheepskins, [they] . . . appeared to enjoy the storm and our discomfiture'.

Through the hail and rain the caravan descended to a hamlet at 12,000 ft for shelter for the night. Cold, wet and no doubt miserable, the party must have looked forward to an early night and sleep. However, this particular inn, as Wilson puts it, 'was chiefly remarkable for the hosts of "Norfolk Howards" it contained'.[26] The insect powder he carried for such eventualities proved utterly useless and the tired travellers were reduced to spending an evening wielding wooden clubs to fight off 'the hungry horde'. Wilson says 'We were glad to escape at dawn and it cannot be said we felt in any sense refreshed after the night's rest.'

In addition to his botanising activities, Wilson also made extensive notes on the different tribes he encountered on his travels. In a letter to Sir William Thiselton-Dyer he describes the life-styles of two primitive tribes he had encountered the previous summer:

They form two tiny states known as Badi and Bawang. Both are under one ruler – a woman. The men are big stalwart fellows somewhat resembling the Tibetans. The women pleasant sturdy creatures, in feature not unlike the peasants of northern Italy.

In Badi the people speak a primitive Tibetan dialect:– in Bawang the language is akin to that of the Lolos. In Bawang the virgins and barren women wear a fringe of beads – about a foot square – in front and a similar fringe behind; the rest of the body being more or less bare. In Badi the same custom obtains but the fringe is deeper. The custom is so

systematically and intentionally indecent that it must have some religious significance –
possibly associated with phallic worship. In Bawang and Badi the marriage customs are
curious and primitive and free love is more or less the rule:– a girl has a child then decides
upon the father. The man of her decision maybe as innocent as Adoni but he has to marry
her all the same! Maternity is always the ratification of marriage. A ceremony is gone
through and in Badi the girl goes to the Mother's home the next day:– in Bawang after a
month has elapsed. She returns and takes the man's name when a child is born. If there is no
child the matter is at an end.[27]

He goes on to say that these people are good masons and that they constructed well-built houses and temples, though the latter, he comments are 'chiefly remarkable for the disgustingly indecent figures they contain'. Wilson, it seems, was not very impressed by the Badi-Bawang folk. Generally, however, the people of Tibet impressed him as friendly and gentle; people with whom he had nothing but pleasant dealings.

The letter from which these extracts were taken was the second he wrote to the then Director of Kew. In December the previous year, James Herbert Veitch had written to Wilson telling him how much Sir William had appreciated his first epistle: 'it is always well to keep in touch with such gentlemen – everybody likes a little attention especially those beyond their first youth and in the so-called high places of the world'.[28] Keeping in touch with Kew in this way would of course stand him in good stead when seeking employment on his return to England.

August and September of this year were spent by Wilson in the mountains bordering the province of Gansu and in the countryside around Songpan:

Having cleared the low country, I got amongst some magnificent mountain ranges covered
with a luxuriant flora, and in places well forested. The sides of these mountains are so steep
that a flying-machine would be necessary to properly explore them. Species of Meconopsis
occurred in plenty, and when collecting the seed we had to tramp about in snow a foot deep.[29]

Wilson's last excursion from Leshan for this second expedition began in November. On this trip, he hoped to secure *Dipelta floribunda*, a member of the Caprifoliaceae family, for cultivation. This was reputed to be a beautiful flowering shrub that was only to be found in the most inaccessible places on mountainous cliffs. To make his task even more difficult, this particular plant only rarely produced fertile seeds. Despite extremely severe weather he again succeeded in the task he had set himself and in little over two weeks was once again back at his base.

It was now time to return to England. His employer had written to him some twelve months previously on the matter of the expedition's termination: 'as soon as you have the result of the autumn of 1904 come right home – I know I can trust you not to leave until you have these – but stay not a moment longer.'[30]

As with his first expedition, Wilson was to experience something of a disappointment in the matter of precedence involving one of his major introductions. In October, he had heard from Herman Spooner of the Veitch organisation

    'CHINESE' WILSON

that an article had appeared in the *Gardeners' Chronicle* giving credit to the first flowering of *Meconopsis integrifolia* to Messrs Bee and Co of Chester. Fortunately, the plants under cultivation for the Veitch firm flowered at the same time and this fact, wired to the *Gardeners' Chronicle*, somewhat saved the situation.

Wilson began his homeward journey on 5 December 1904 and reached Yichang early in the New Year. He arrived back in England in March 1905 and had to his credit some 510 numbers of seeds and 2,400 numbers of herbarium specimens.[31] The expedition had in every way been a success.

John Gould Veitch, a nephew of Harry James Veitch, was one of the members of the family who passed instructions to Wilson, and to whom he wrote on his travels.

Chapter Three
With Vasculum, Camera and Gun

The Veitch firm were once again delighted with the results of Wilson's work in China and they marked their appreciation in tangible form. He was presented with a gold pin in the form of *Meconopsis integrifolia*, the flower of which was made up of five solid gold petals, encrusted with forty-one diamonds. In 1906, the firm further honoured him with the presentation of the Veitch Memorial Medal, an award much prized in horticultural circles. The citation read: 'To E H Wilson in recognition of his great services to Horticulture by his discovery and introduction of new plants from China'.

On his third trip to China, Wilson sought out new ornamental shrubs. This one, *Ceratostigma willmottianum*, has rich blue flowers which appear in July and continue into the autumn. It was introduced from western China in 1907.

Ernest and Nellie lived here, at 77 Gloucester Road, Kew, when he was working at the Imperial Institute of Science. Their only child, Muriel Primrose, was born here in the spring of 1906.

Initially Wilson found temporary employment working with his collections at Coombe Wood and at the Kew Herbarium. In January 1906 he accepted a government appointment as botanical assistant at the Imperial Institute of Science in London. Here his work would involve examining and cataloguing botanical collections forwarded from Hong Kong. The Wilsons settled down in Kew at 77 Gloucester Road, a modest little house set in a pretty tree-lined terrace only ten minutes' walk from the Royal Botanic Gardens.

For a time it must have seemed to Nellie Wilson that her husband was at last about to settle down. To further mark his newly found domesticity the Wilsons started a family. The Wilsons' only child was born on 21 May 1906 and it so happened that on this particular day one of Wilson's plants from China flowered for the first time at Kew. Wilson's daughter was named Muriel Primrose after this flower and the plant was named, *Primula wilsonii*[1] for its discoverer. This was the very first of Wilson's introductions to bear his name.

Wilson, it would seem, was very happy living in Kew. In later life, after many years of living in America, he still liked to refer to himself in letters to English friends as a 'Kewite'. Despite spending over twenty years in the United States he never took up American citizenship and he told friends that it was his intention to one day return to his 'dear beloved Kew'.

Wilson's retirement from the field, however, was to be a temporary one. Charles Sprague Sargent, the Director of the Arnold Arboretum in Boston, had in mind an expedition to China of his own. Sargent was keen to expand the Arboretum and further raise its standing as a major centre for botanical research. He was aware of the success of the latest Veitch expeditions and he regarded China as a rich source of new material. In England, Sargent sought the services of a collector of the right calibre for this work. Ernest Wilson seemed to have all the qualities he required for the leader of such an expedition. Sargent's initial approaches to Wilson, however, were not received with the enthusiasm he had hoped for.

Wilson, it would appear, had felt that the secure employment he had obtained at the Imperial Institute was not something he could throw over at short notice. There were other considerations also. To accept Sargent's proposal would mean yet another lengthy separation from his wife and, of course, his young daughter.

Sargent, however, was not a man to be put off easily. He now considered Wilson to be the best man for the task he had in mind and he was more determined than ever to secure his services. After consulting with friends of Wilson, he formed the opinion that the offer of a larger salary might work in his favour.

Miss Ellen Willmott, a keen amateur gardener and enthusiast of Wilson's work, had told Sargent of another possible obstacle which might need to be overcome, namely Mrs Wilson. 'It was very sad that such a promising man should be hampered by such an ignorant short sighted wife at such an early stage of his career,' she wrote.[2]

Whether or not Nellie objected, Wilson finally agreed to undertake a two-year expedition to China for a sum of $US 7500 (£1500 in 1906). As a further inducement, Sargent had strongly hinted that a permanent post for Wilson would be available at the Arnold Arboretum on his return. 'So you have captured me after all,' Wilson wrote to Sargent. 'Twelve months ago I would not have believed it possible for anyone to have persuaded me into revisiting China on any terms'.[3]

The nature of this expedition was to be somewhat different to those taken on behalf of the Veitch nurseries. This time commercial factors would be secondary to scientific ones. Sargent was interested primarily in woody plants and it was his wish that Wilson would cover as much territory as possible to obtain interesting specimens. The gathering of herbarium material would also be of great importance in making the expedition worth while from a scientific standpoint. To this end Wilson was instructed to make up several sets of the material collected, some of which could be used as exchange items to send to botanical institutions around the world.

Sargent was also keen that a good photographic record of the expedition should be made: 'A good set of photographs are really about as important as anything you can bring back with you. I hope therefore, you will not fail to provide yourself with the very best possible instrument you can, irrespective of cost'.[4]

A neighbour of the Wilsons in Kew at this time was the highly regarded photographer E J Wallis, who lived at 42 Gloucester Road. Wallis had carried out a good deal of work for the Royal Botanic Gardens and had also obtained regular

Although Wilson used photography principally as a means of recording his observations in the field, many of his photographs demonstrate a high level of competence. Left: a bamboo suspension bridge in western Sichuan. Right: a small town in western Hubei in winter.

commissions for the *Gardeners' Chronicle*. He had prepared the plates for the history of the Veitch nurseries, *Hortus Veitchii*, and in later years was to prepare the plates for some of Wilson's books.

For this first expedition on behalf of the Arnold Arboretum, Wilson employed Wallis's services for all the photographic processing work. Consignments of exposed plates were shipped directly to Wallis, though the actual developing was not carried out until Wilson's return from China. It would seem that Wilson wanted to ensure that the plates were individually processed to obtain the very best results possible.

Before this expedition Wilson would have to be regarded as a novice in the art of photography. Prior to setting out for China he would certainly have found the need for a few basic lessons in the handling of the large-plate cameras necessary for producing high-quality photographs. Wallis would have been the obvious choice of tutor and he probably also gave Wilson some useful advice on the selection of a suitable instrument to take with him. Although Wilson had very little time to master the complexities of the equipment before setting out, the photographs he sent back from his travels show a high level of technical skill and a real appreciation of what makes an interesting picture.[5]

On this expedition, Wilson took two cameras. His principal instrument was a high-quality whole-plate camera made by Sanderson, a leading maker. He also took with him a small folding Kodak, which used the recently developed roll film. A few examples of photographs taken with this instrument are to be found amongst Wilson's personal effects and they are of a noticeably poorer quality than the photographs made with the Sanderson camera.

In early December 1906, Wilson was *en route* once more for Boston, where he arrived just before Christmas. A formal agreement between Wilson and the University of Harvard was drawn up and signed on 27 December. In this document Wilson was contracted to spend two full winter and summer seasons in China or stay there until the end of 1908.

The expedition was to be financed by subscription. Fourteen contributions of $US 1000 and one of $US 7000 were received from the Friends of the Arnold Arboretum, together with numerous smaller donations. Three contributions were received from enthusiasts in England, including one of £200 from Ellen Willmott. It is interesting to note, however, that no contribution was forthcoming from the firm of Veitch. Those who did provide money could expect to receive plant material on the completion of the expedition. To this end Wilson was given instructions to gather orchids for one contributor and lily bulbs for others.

Once in the field, Wilson was expected to co-operate with the United States Department of Agriculture's man in China, Frank Meyer. In a quid pro quo, Wilson operating in Sichuan and Hubei would obtain seeds and propagating material of economically important plants for the department, while Meyer, in the Wutai mountains further north, would collect cones and conifers for the Arboretum.

In addition to the arrangement made with the Department of Agriculture, Wilson would have administrative responsibility for a young collector sent out to China by Harvard's Museum of Comparative Zoology. His name was Walter Zappey and his instructions were to gather bird skins and animal pelts for the museum.

Wilson left for China within days of signing the contract for the expedition, travelling via Honolulu and Yokohama. A postcard sent to his wife from Yokohama, dated January 1907, shows just the Kew address, apparently written in haste, and no message. Once Ernest was in the interior of China, Nellie Wilson could not expect even such flimsy evidence as this of her husband's continued good health.

From Yokohama, Wilson sailed for Shanghai, where he arrived on 4 February. Here he met up with Frank Meyer, as planned. Meyer, it turned out, was a rather dour Dutchman whom Wilson could not take to. In a letter to Sargent dated just a week after first making Meyer's acquaintance, Wilson wrote that Meyer had 'no sense of humour' and that he had 'very little sympathy for the yellow race and ignores their manners and customs'.[6] Wilson also observed that: 'Whilst he [Meyer] glories in roughing it and in the superiority of the white race, I fancy he will modify his views and methods somewhat after a time. I seriously hope so for when he comes to reside amongst the Chinese he will find that his present methods are not calculated to get the best from his men'. Meyer, operating to the north of Wilson, in the province of Shanxi, had varied success as a collector. He managed a good harvest of economic plant material but complained that the region was 'utterly barren' when it came to ornamentals.

Sargent was disappointed by Meyer's efforts, a disappointment which later changed to something bordering on contempt when he discovered important omissions in the material he sent back. Several previously unknown species of *Picea*, *Larix* and *Pinus* were found among Meyer's herbarium specimens, but he had neglected to collect seed for them.

It would appear that Meyer never did mend his ways when it came to his handling of the Chinese. He disappeared one night in 1918 while journeying down-river between Hankou and Nanjing and in a letter to Wilson Sargent speculated that 'some of the Chinamen may have thrown him overboard'.[7]

Wilson's dealings with Walter Zappey were to be more pleasant. Their association was to last over two years, from February 1907 to March 1909, when Zappey finally left China. The fact that they were collecting fauna as well as flora gave ample opportunity for sport with dog and gun, and Wilson, armed with his 12-bore, and Zappey with his rifle (for larger quarry) had many successful and, it would seem, enjoyable hunting trips together in the interior of China.

Wilson wrote at length about these excursions in the second volume of *A Naturalist in Western China*, and he often glories in the day's kill:

My companion, Mr Zappey, was seated on the prow of the boat and with his field-glasses scanning the cliffs from time-to-time. 'This looks ideal country for Goral,' he said to me,

'CHINESE' WILSON

WITH VASCULUM, CAMERA AND GUN

standing near him. 'Has anyone ever seen them hereabouts?' 'I don't know, but there is no record of anyone having shot one,' I replied. Scarcely had the words left my mouth when Zappey quietly said 'There's one!'

He rushed into the cabin and secured his rifle; meanwhile the crew shortened sail. The animal stood under the lee of a cliff some 500 feet above the river; it was about 4.30 in the afternoon. There was considerable weigh on the boat and Zappey's first shot struck a little above and in front of the Goral, and the beast scarcely heeded it. The second shot was again a little high, and immediately in front, and the animal swung round, ran a few yards, and then stopped, half facing us. The third shot found its mark; the soft nosed bullet passed anglewise through the jugular vein far into the body and the Goral sank stone dead in his tracks. It was a pretty shot, and from the motion of the boat, not an easy one.[8]

Occasionally Wilson and Zappey stalked larger game. Wilson tells us in his earliest writings[9] that quite a variety of carnivores were to be found in western China, including the leopard and the black bear. He says that in western Hubei the odd tiger was not uncommon and that their skins were often to be found for sale. Wilson himself obtained one as a trophy and from the measurements he gives it would seem that the animal was a relatively small specimen.

While travelling through the Changyang and Badong areas in 1907 he had been shown the bloody remains of an old woman who had been killed and partially eaten by one of these animals. A tigress and her cub were located in a local cave and Wilson and his companion had been invited to be in on the kill:

To capture the lordly tiger the Chinese collect together to the number of a hundred or more and make a tremendous noise by shooting and beating gongs. When satisfied that the beast is

The *Harvard*, the boat that Wilson purchased on his first expedition to China for the Arnold Arboretum. In this photograph, taken in 1907, Wilson is seen with his associate for this trip, Walter Zappey.

'CHINESE' WILSON

ensconced within a cave they build a large bonfire at the entrance in order to smoke the animal out. All the hunters are armed with guns, spears, clubs, etc., and when the stupefied tiger attempts to escape they make a concentrated and bold attempt upon him.[10]

If the reader is of the opinion that this sounds to have been a somewhat uneven-handed contest, he or she can be reassured by Wilson's final observation on the tiger hunt: 'As often as not he gets away and frequently some of the people get badly mauled.'

As with his first expedition, Wilson purchased a boat at Yichang. This time he registered it as the *Harvard*. Here he was also able to engage the necessary labour and was fortunate in being able to secure the services of several old hands from his previous expeditions. After a brief excursion to the south-west of Yichang to test equipment and acquaint his men with collecting techniques, Wilson decided upon a longer trip through north-western Hubei.

Leaving Yichang in May 1907, he journeyed first to Xingshan and then, following the Hubei–Sichuan border, crossed into Shaanxi province. He then doubled back into Hubei and returned to Yichang via Zhushan and Fang Xian. In all this was a trip of some 500 miles, and it took nearly six weeks.

This proved to be an extremely hard trip for the expedition. The countryside was poverty-stricken and food was almost unobtainable. Not surprisingly, they were charged famine prices for the little they could find. The flora encountered, however, was a rich one and Wilson and his collectors succeeded in amassing some 3500 specimens of plant material.

For much of the remaining summer months, Wilson collected in Jiangxi province, in the region of the Lushan hills, close to Jiujiang and some 140 miles down-river from Hankou. In July, while working in this region – which was an area where Père David had collected, some forty years previously – Wilson found what proved to be a new species of lily, later to be named by him *Lilium cathayanum* and now put into the genus *Cardiocrinum*. This particular lily had been first noted in this area by Père David and later by Henry in western Hubei. Henry, however, had mistaken it for a variety of *L. giganteum* (now *Cardiocrinum giganteum*).[11] In the same area, Wilson had hoped to collect a variety of *Lilium speciosum* first noted here by Père David in August 1868, but he searched in vain.[12]

The month of September 1907 was a bad one for Wilson. He suffered a severe bout of malaria which caused him to retire to his bed for three weeks. This illness greatly reduced his stamina, so that his collecting, other than in the close vicinity of Yichang, was severely curtailed. This of course was a great blow to the expedition, coming as it did during the fruiting season, when seed-gathering ought to have been the primary activity. His men did the best they could but they could not be expected to achieve other than mediocre results. Wilson had to content himself with preparing herbarium specimens and in packing up material for shipment to the United States.

Wilson had hoped to make up for lost time with an early start to the spring collecting season in 1908. There were, however, a number of minor irritations which delayed the expedition. One problem involved his supply of ammunition. The Chinese authorities had placed a restriction on the number of cartridges which could be imported into mainland China. Without a plentiful supply of rifle and shotgun ammunition, Zappey's expedition was certain to have reduced success. Wilson succeeded in overcoming this problem, only to find that serious faults had developed in the *Harvard*. Repairs would have to be made before it could be considered serviceable for a long hard river trip, and it was March before the expedition could get under way, two weeks later than Wilson had planned.

He journeyed the now familiar route by river to the union of the Yangtze and the Min, and then northwards to Leshan, his base on previous expeditions to the region. From here he intended to explore the fertile valley of the Min and the rich Chengdu plain.

Early summer found Wilson in the city of Chengdu. This was one of the most interesting and historic cities he saw in western China. Marco Polo had visited it six centuries earlier[13] and had been impressed by its wealth. It was still an important centre of commerce and Wilson gives a vivid description of it. He seems to have been particularly impressed by its fortifications, but he also gives an account of the internal organisation of the city, and shows how wealthy it was.

It was divided into a number of trade quarters, so that all the dealers in silk goods or furs, for example, were to be found in one area, and craftsmen of different types – potters, boot-makers, goldsmiths and silversmiths – were to be found in

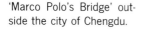
'Marco Polo's Bridge' outside the city of Chengdu.

'CHINESE' WILSON

other, separate areas. Lacquered and gilded shop signs advertised the businesses of prosperous shopkeepers. Sedan chairs were widely used, but unlike Wilson's chair, which lifted him only a foot or so off the ground, these were carried shoulder-high, so that the passenger actually sat above the heads of the crowds of pedestrians.

The surrounding countryside contained some of the richest and most fertile soil in China, fed by a series of ancient irrigation works kept in excellent repair. Wilson reports, however, that these were the only public works to be treated with respect. The roads were poorly maintained and as a result were extremely dusty in dry weather and ankle-deep in mud in the wet. Bridges, however, were marvels of engineering, and Wilson mentions one, just outside the east gate of Chengdu, that was probably also described by Marco Polo.

Setting out from Chengdu, Wilson had decided on an expedition westwards, first north-west to Guan Xian, and then south-west to Kangding, that would take about three weeks. Wilson wrote that his caravan for this expedition consisted of 'eighteen carrying coolies and one head-coolie, two chairs, two handymen, an escort of two soldiers, my Boy, and self, making a party of thirty all told.'[14] (Actually, assuming the 'chairs' each required two men, the party totals only twenty-nine. The last member of the party would have been Walter Zappey.)

He arrived at Guan Xian on 16 June and after speedily completing his remaining preparations was on his way by late afternoon. The next day's march was a long one – some 18 miles over very poor roads. At Guan Xian he had reduced the coolies' loads, and a little later he had hired an extra hand but in spite of this his men could hardly stagger along.

A temple on the outskirts of Guan Xian in western Sichuan.

The flora so far had been poor from a collecting standpoint, though the party had been fortunate enough to come across wild strawberries growing in abundance. This discovery would have provided a welcome supplement to the expedition's usual plain diet.[15]

They reached their lodgings for the night at 6 p.m. and Wilson was pleased to find that the accommodation on offer was 'roomy' and the people there 'both courteous and attentive'.

The following day began with heavy rain and the 15-mile march was to be a damp and miserable one. However, during the day, Wilson had been able to collect some interesting specimens, and he recalls meeting *en route* some labourers heavily laden with huge logs of hemlock-spruce and larch. He recorded the measurement of one of these as over 18 ft long and was astounded at the way the men carried them over the treacherous mountain tracks.

On the morning of 19 June the expedition began a difficult mountain climb to the summit of Niutou Shan. The plants they found proved worth collecting, though Wilson's botanising was hampered by thick mist. Amongst other species, he noted *Clematis montana* 'Grandiflora' and *Deutzia rubens*. The trees, he observed, consisted mainly of hemlock spruce with the occasional silver fir and yew. As the party descended to their lodgings for the evening, he saw that much tree felling was in progress and that it was apparently from here that the log-bearers encountered earlier had come.

The following two days' tramp was over difficult and dangerous roads. At times, Wilson and his men had to cross rotting log bridges where one wrong step could precipitate the unwary into a torrent of ice-cold water.

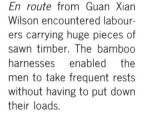

En route from Guan Xian Wilson encountered labourers carrying huge pieces of sawn timber. The bamboo harnesses enabled the men to take frequent rests without having to put down their loads.

'CHINESE' WILSON

The next stop was at another 'spartan' hostel. 'Shelter for the night and a fire to cook food and dry clothing are all that these places afford', he comments.[16] His men occasionally purchased opium at these stops and presumably smoked themselves into a stupor which dulled the edge of their discomfort.

After two days of gradual ascent, Wilson and his men entered the alpine zone. At 11,500 ft he came across *Meconopsis integrifolia* covering mile upon mile of mountainside. This was the yellow poppywort which he had laboured so hard to obtain in 1903. Wilson halted for the evening of 22 June at a place part temple and part inn, kept by a priest 'to whose clothing and person' Wilson says 'water was evidently a stranger'.

Beyond this hostel lay the dreaded mountain known as Pan-lan Shan, with its infamous pass. This was a place of evil reputation, and many travellers had perished in its rarefied atmosphere and bone-chilling mist. 'Silence reigns in these lonely alpine regions,' Wilson wrote in his journal, 'a silence so oppressive as to be almost felt and only broken on rare occasions by the song of some lark soaring skywards'.

On 27 June, Wilson and his men arrived at Xiaojin (known to Wilson as MonKong Ting), where he had intended to rest over for the day. The town was crowded, however, and Wilson found his inn made intolerable by 'persons who were noisy over their cups . . . rendering sleep well-nigh an impossibility'. At daybreak he decided to press on to Danba.

Not long after the day's journey had begun the party came to a bridge that was being repaired. The waters beneath it were deep and turbulent and the crossing involved traversing two very uneven logs with only a thin rope to act as a handrail. A local official was kind enough to supply labour to carry the expedition's im-

The combined hostel and temple near the summit of Pan-lan-shan. Shrouded in freezing mist, this was one of the most inhospitable places Wilson visited during his travels in China.

pedimenta across: 'Everything came over all right but my followers clung to the local men like grim death, the majority shaking in their nervous fright.' Wilson's dog was lashed to a flat board and carried across on a man's back: 'He struggled violently, and the man only just managed to get him over before he got half loose. I walked over behind the dog and was relieved when the 30 yards across the yawning gulf were safely passed.'[17] Wilson rewarded the local men 'to their astonished delight' with a present of a thousand cash.[18]

On 30 June the caravan arrived at Danba, then known as Romi Chango, a 'poor unwalled, straggling town of about 130 houses'. The town was frequented by the Badi-Bawang folk described in chapter 2. His accommodation in this town was clean and relatively quiet after Xiaojin and he decided to stay over for an extra day.

The following morning Wilson received a request from the town magistrate for medicine to ease a severe bout of stomach cramps and vomiting. Wilson was happy to oblige and sent the ailing man a quantity of Epsom salts and an opiate. Apparently such requests were common at this time and Wilson advises any traveller in China to carry simple remedies to dispense when called to do so. The efficacy of European materia medica was becoming recognised by the Chinese and such assistance was always greeted with gratitude. Wilson later received news that the magistrate was feeling better and on the way to making a full recovery.

The journey from Danba was to be a particularly vile one. Recent storms had completely washed the roads away in places and caused extensive flooding, and Wilson and his men had to wade through water that was sometimes as much as 4 ft deep. To make matters worse, some of the roads led past houses where there were open sewers, and the refuse from these spilled out into the floodwater, so that the caravan might be calf-deep in dung and refuse. 'Such filthy surroundings are characteristic of Tibetan houses,' Wilson declares, but the waste was probably intended to be collected and used as fertiliser.

The 4th and 5th of July were spent resting at a little hamlet at 10,000 ft. The house where they lodged was a three-storeyed building with walls built of shale and a flat mud roof. Wilson provides a colourful description of its interior: 'Entering through a low doorway we had first to traverse a yard filled with cattle dung, then a piggery where a steep ladder led upwards to a couple of dark empty rooms in which we installed ourselves.'[19] The rooms contained not a stick of furniture, and he and his men had to make their own comforts. 'Tibetans squat on the floor for their meals and so have no use for tables or chairs,' Wilson comments. Their hostess here was a cheerful if dirty person whose pleasant disposition and frequent laughter greatly amused Wilson and his men and did much to lighten their humour.

While they were resting from their journey, Wilson took the opportunity to photograph some of the more interesting trees in the area. Even this work was to prove excessively hard. The undergrowth round about was extremely dense, and Wilson and his men found themselves spending an hour or more hacking at the bamboo jungle in order to expose a single plate.

56

Sometimes, when hostel accommodation was not available, the expedition would camp out for the night. The evening of 6 July was to be just such an occasion:

We camped near the tree-limit, at about 12,000 feet altitude, and erected a small hut of spruce boughs under a large Silver Fir tree. My Boy preferred to pass the night in his chair and the men arranged themselves around a log fire. The neighbourhood has an evil reputation for highway robbers, but we felt sure there was small possibility of any attack on us being made.[20]

The night was cold and wet and even his dog suffered badly: 'he refused to eat his supper and I never saw him so utterly miserable'.

Wilson was amazed by the indifference shown by his men when it came to the business of making camping out tolerable. Not one of them attempted to construct even the simplest of shelters, he notes in his journal, and they would even have allowed the fire to go out, had not one of the Tibetan guides attended to it.

Continuing their climb, the party finally reached the tree-line and beyond that at 14,500 ft, the eternal snows. From here Wilson was able to view 'sinister'-looking glaciers and in the far distance, rising through the mist, the town of Kangding.

Wilson had been in Kangding in 1903 and 1904. This time he was to make the acquaintance of the king of Chiala, whose residence was in the town, and who was the ruler of a group of tribes to be found west of the Dadu River. Wilson and Zappey were presented to the king, who took a keen interest in their work. He was particularly intrigued by Zappey's taxidermy and, Wilson says, was delighted to receive a stuffed hoopoe from Zappey as a parting gift.

The remaining weeks of July were spent in investigating the area around Kangding and the fertile valley of the Dadu River. He also revisited Wa Shan, where he had botanised on his previous expedition for the Veitches. At the end of the month he returned to the city of Chengdu and spent some weeks investigating the rich flora of the surrounding countryside.

At the end of August, Wilson journeyed south once more via Ya'an and Hongya to his base at Leshan. From here he planned to make what would be an arduous excursion through a desolate region known to the Chinese as the Laolin. The Laolin or 'wilderness' was a roughly triangular tract of land which had its northern limit between the mountains of Wa-Wu and Emei and which stretched southwards as far as Wa Shan. It was Wilson's intention to cross the Laolin in a diagonal line south-west from its north-eastern corner to a point on the main road to Fulin and near to Wa Shan.

Wilson and his men left Leshan on 4 September and reached the edge of the Laolin the following evening. Progress was slow as they hacked through the dense fern jungle, tormented by mosquitoes, and on the third day they only covered 8 miles. They were gradually ascending the summit of the ridge called Tsao Shan, from which they could glimpse the dark form of Wa-Wu thrusting upwards through the cloud and mist. So far, the expedition was not proving very rewarding from the botanical point of view, though Wilson did find a new species of *Castanopsis*.

He had already ascended the peaks of Emei Shan and Wa Shan on previous trips to this region. It was now his intention to explore the third mountain of the trio. He expected the two-day march to the summit of Wa-Wu to be a hard one, so he gave orders for the loads carried by the caravan to be lightened. The morning of the 9th was begun early and the caravan succeeded in covering nearly 10 miles before noon. Halting at the foot of the mountain, the party put up for the evening at a

temple . . . built of wood, very old, and in poor repair. A priest and one attendant were in charge; the rooms, though dingy and damp were alive with fleas. But since there is no other accommodation between this place and the summit it was necessary to make the best of things. I had my bed arranged in a large hall where three huge images of Buddha looked down benignly upon me.[21]

A view of the mountain Wa-Wu (the furthest peak here), which Wilson visited in September 1908. He had already explored its sisters, Emei Shan and Wa Shan, on previous expeditions.

Heavy rain fell all night, adding to their discomfort. The weather had failed to improve by morning and the ascent of the mountain was begun in a steady downpour, adding to the difficulty of the climb.

Wa-Wu was to prove disappointing botanically, the flora comparing un-favourably with what he had found on its two sisters. Heavy rain and dense mist hampered his efforts and he was unable to see anything save that which was 'encompassed in a perspective of 30 yards'. Drenched to the skin, they found shelter for the night in another temple.

This one was in the charge of a novice priest, who made them most welcome. Many pilgrims visited the mountain in the months of June and July but hardly any at other times of the year, so no doubt he was glad of the company. After building a fire for his visitors he did all that he could to bring some cheer to Wilson and his men.

After spending a further day on the summit to complete his work, Wilson began the journey back. Some of the way lay through dense bamboo jungle where it was easy to lose the track. Getting lost slowed them down: at one stage, when they failed to make the planned mileage, it looked as if they might have to spend a night out in the woods, but as darkness fell they saw the glare from a charcoal-burner's camp on the far side of a stream:

Scrambling somehow down the steep slope, and across the torrent, we quickly reached this haven of shelter. It proved a wretched hovel, but the warmth from the charcoal pit was comforting since we, and all our belongings, were wet through. My bed was fixed up in a shed where prepared charcoal was stored, the men taking possession of the hut, thankful that a refuge of some sort had been found.[22]

Though the shed roof leaked freely, Wilson managed to use oil sheets to keep his bedding dry and enjoy a reasonable night's sleep.

The final part of the journey across the Laolin was equally slow – one day an eleven-hour march covered only 10 miles – and Wilson wrote 'Except on odd occasions I saw nothing outside a radius of 50 yards.'[23] The appalling weather conditions had prevented any really useful investigations, and overall the expedition had been a disappointing one.

The next two months were spent exploring further the Chengdu plain and the valley of the Dadu River. In the middle of November Wilson received disturbing news of the sudden death of the emperor, Guangxu, possibly from poison. This event was followed up the next day by the death of the empress dowager, Cixi, also in mysterious circumstances. Wilson wrote to Sargent:

Her [the Empress's] death means that certain all-powerful ministers and Viceroys will control the destinies of China for some years to come. Jealousies carefully hidden whilst the late Empress ruled will now hark out and it is hard to prophesy what may happen . . . I think China will be a very good country to be out of until the new Emperor is firmly established on the throne.[24]

He had been in China at the time of the Boxer Rebellion and was fully aware of how quickly trouble could spread. The building of the Chinese railways with foreign loans had caused bitter resentment and now that resentment might have the opportunity to spill over into yet another bloodbath.

As Wilson's third expedition drew to a close, Sargent made preparations for the dispatch of a new man to China, to explore the northern provinces where Meyer had obtained such poor results. Wilson received word of William Purdom's appointment from Sargent in the New Year. From his subsequent reply[25] it would appear that he received the news with very mixed feelings. In his letter he says that he is glad that the offer of a further season in China had not been made to him, since acceptance 'would have completely broken up my wife'. Later in the same letter, however, he confesses to 'a slight feeling of chagrin at being passed over so completely in favour of another and without a word of warning.' From the rest of the letter it would seem that one of Wilson's chief concerns was that others might view his replacement as a reflection on the quality of the work he had done.

At Yichang Wilson arranged for the crating of equipment and plant material for the long journey to America. Part of the consignment consisted of several thousand lily bulbs packed carefully in clay. These, unfortunately, were stowed in the hold of the ship in close proximity to a cargo of raw hides. On arrival in the United States they were found to have rotted and were completely useless. This collection included a quantity of bulbs of the regal lily, *Lilium regale*, which Wilson felt might have proved to be a major introduction. For this plant, Wilson would return again to China and for its eventual successful introduction he would pay a very high price.

This time he returned to Europe by train. He started the journey from Peking in April, travelling on to Harbin in Manchuria, from where he could link up with the Eastern China Rail Road. This connected with the famous Trans-Siberian Railway, which ran right through to Moscow. Conditions would have been spartan, with no sleeping accommodation, and no doubt the journey was very tiring.

From Moscow he went on to St Petersburg, Berlin and Paris. At each of these cities he stopped off to visit nurseries and botanical collections. This was something of a public relations exercise for Wilson, on behalf of the Arnold Arboretum. The intention would have been to make useful contracts with other institutions for the exchange of herbaria and other plant materials. He arrived back at Kew on 17 May, in time to combine a reunion with Nellie and a celebration of his daughter's third birthday, the child he had last seen as a six-month-old baby.

One of his first tasks on his return was to visit Coombe Wood, to check the progress of some of his earliest introductions. He also spent time with the Kew photographer Wallis, working on the sixty dozen plates he had shipped home that March. The results, it seems, were excellent, and included over 500 plant studies.

His major concern was now a financial one. His contract with Harvard University had expired and he was in need of a new job. Sargent had offered him temporary employment at the Arboretum, working up his collections, but the salary being offered was a good deal less than Wilson could have expected. However, with no other offer to hand, he reluctantly accepted, and in September 1909 he sailed once more for Boston, this time accompanied by his wife and daughter.

Muriel Wilson, photographed by E J Wallis. When Wilson returned to Britain in 1909, he had been away from his family for two and a half years.

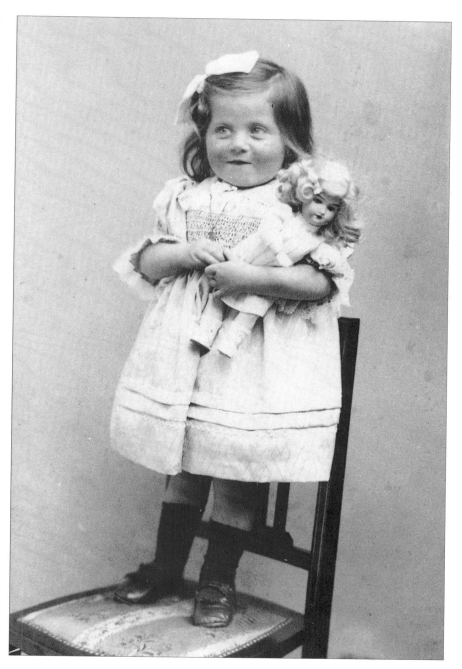

The hunt for the regal lily, *Lilium regale*, was particularly hazardous. This beautiful plant was to be one of Wilson's most successful introductions, but the accident he suffered while searching for it in the Min gorge crippled him and put an end to his plant-hunting days in China.

Chapter Four
Risking All for the Regal Lily

The Arnold Arboretum had been established in 1872, principally through the generosity of James Arnold, a merchant of New Bedford, Massachusetts, who had endowed the University of Harvard with a sum of money to be devoted to the development of a scientific station for the study of trees. Charles Sprague Sargent had been appointed as its first director and largely as a result of his enthusiasm and energy it had become a major centre of botanical research.

Wilson's work at the Arboretum was mainly concerned with taxonomic and nomenclatural research, which must have seemed rather pedestrian after the dangers and hardships of plant hunting in China. His salary was less than he had expected, and the cost of living in the United States was beginning to cause him some concern. He complained to Sargent about his salary, but to no avail. In May 1909 Sargent had hinted that he might require Wilson to undertake yet another journey to China, and he may have thought it not in the interests of the Arboretum to make Wilson too comfortable in a desk job.

The problem was resolved at the beginning of the New Year, when Sargent did in fact propose another trip to China, and Wilson accepted. It would mean yet another lengthy separation from Nellie and Muriel, but possibly he felt he had little choice in the matter.

This photograph of Wilson's caravan was taken in 1910, during his fourth expedition to China. His head man or 'Boy' is seated in the middle of the front row.

One of the principal aims for this expedition was to secure a good collection of conifer seeds, and Wilson was to seek out new species of fir. He was also required to obtain further quantities of the bulbs of *Lilium regale*, to replace the ill-fated shipment from the previous trip. Since arrangements for this expedition were conducted at the Arboretum, there is much less in the way of documentation concerning Wilson's instructions. By this time, however, Sargent knew his man well enough to place complete trust in his abilities, and it is likely that Wilson was given much more latitude in the conduct of this trip to China.

The Wilsons left Boston at the end of March 1910 and journeyed to England. Having safely installed his wife and four-year-old daughter with his parents and sisters in Birmingham, Wilson set off once more for the Far East. He returned the same way as he had travelled back from previous expedition, using the Trans-Siberian Railway. After a brief stay in Peking, he arrived in Yichang on 1 June 1910.

Once at his base, he speedily set about the now familiar preparations for a lengthy trip through the Chinese interior. At Yichang he was able to obtain the services of some of his experienced men from previous visits and within a matter of days he was ready to begin the expedition proper: 'On 4th June I left Ichang for Chengtu, via a new route through the wilds of north-west Hupeh. With 600 miles of overland travel ahead the caravan had been fitted up with all the skill at my command, and with enthusiasm to spur us on I felt that the difficulties would not prove insurmountable.'[1]

Wilson describes the route to be taken as an 'absolute terra-incognita' which had never before been attempted in its entirety. Altogether the journey would occupy some eight weeks through the very worst of rough, mountainous country.

After only one day, some of the coolies gave up and others had to be found. Each day's march proved more arduous than the previous one, as vile roads gave way to treacherous mountain tracks. The weather was hot and humid but frequent showers provided some relief.

As on previous trips, the accommodation available *en route* was spartan in the extreme and difficult to obtain. On the evening of 9 June the expedition halted at Xiangtan, a village that was an important trade centre on a tributary of the Yangtze. Its name means 'fragrant rapid', but Wilson notes in his journal that 'The waters may perhaps be sweet, but the village is foul and stinking.'

Occasionally it would seem that Wilson was prepared to adopt a rather high-handed attitude towards some of the people he encountered on his travels. At his lodgings at Xiangtan he informs us that 'an objectionable coolie had to be evicted' before he and his men could settle down for the night. Sometimes the owner of a farmhouse would be reluctant to provide Wilson's party with accommodation. Wilson would then adopt the military expedient of simply commandeering the building. On one of his marches across the province of Sichuan he and his men halted at a village where half the houses had recently been destroyed by fire.

Wilson writes of this visit in his typically matter-of-fact way: 'We had some difficulty in obtaining lodgings, the only decent place being full and the occupants unwilling to move. After a little time persuasive insistance won, and we settled down comfortably, if crowded.'[2]

They left Xiangtan on 10 June, and, crossing the river by ferry, entered a narrow valley which eventually became 'a wild entrancing gorge'. In this area Wilson was able to collect many interesting specimens, including *Rehmannia henryi*, a herb less than a foot tall, with large, white, foxglove-like flowers. He also gathered a sulphur-yellow-flowered form of *Rosa banksiae*.

The following day Wilson took time to explore a massive limestone peak known as Wan-tiao Shan. On the summit of this mountain he discovered a new species of lilac, *Syringa verrucosa* (now called *S. julianae*). Altogether he collected some 'forty odd' different plants, which he regarded as ample reward for what had been a very hard climb.

On this trip he had also been given instructions to make careful notes on any interesting commercial enterprises engaged in by the Chinese. One example of this was the cultivation of the edible fungus known as the Jew's ear fungus:

Oak saplings, [Quercus variabilis], about 6 inches thick, are cut down, trimmed of their branches, and cut into staves 8 to 10 feet long. These are allowed to lie on the ground for several months, where they become infected with the mycelium of the fungus. They are then stacked slantingly in scores or thereabouts and the fruitifications of the fungus develop. These are ear-shaped and gelatinous and are by the Chinese esteemed a delicacy. I tried them, but did not find them very palatable, and the experiment resulted in a bad stomach-ache![3]

Wilson describes this as 'a good specimen of rural homesteads in the wilds of Hupeh'. He and his caravan stayed here on the evening of 11 June 1910.

'CHINESE' WILSON

Bee-keeping was another activity to draw Wilson's attention. Hives were constructed from hollowed-out logs of silver fir. Wilson tells us that no attempt is made to separate the honey from the beeswax, the honeycomb being eaten exactly as it was removed from the hive.[4]

By 22 June, the expedition found itself on the 'Great Salt Road'. The province of Sichuan was rich in salt wells, and for many centuries salt had been the principal commodity in these parts. In *A Naturalist in Western China*, Wilson describes how the salt wells were worked and estimates annual production at some 300,000 tons.[5] Despite the wealth and fertility of the region, however, food was hard to come by, and Wilson reports that they had to pay famine prices for the little they could find.

On 23 June the expedition entered eastern Sichuan, an area of towering limestone cliffs and spectacular scenery. Wilson's description of the view from the little village he called Hsao-Pingtsze, itself perched on the edge of a precipice and walled in on three sides by steep cliffs, gives a vivid picture of this dramatic landscape and shows his writing at its very best:

It was only some 30 yards from our hut to the edge of the precipice, and the view from this point is one of the most extraordinary and wonderful my eyes have ever beheld. Below me (some 4,000 feet the morrow proved) at an acute angle lay a small village with a considerable river flowing past it. Beyond this was range upon range of bare, treeless, sharp-edged ridges, averaging 5,000 to 6,000 feet in height, with outstanding higher peaks and grander ranges in the beyond. The rocks are mainly of limestone, white, grey and reddish, giving a bizarre appearance to the whole scene. Never have I looked upon a wilder,

The hostels where Wilson stayed were always rough. This example, in the mountains east of Songpan, would have provided fairly spartan accommodation. Wilson can be seen at the far right of the photograph.

more savage and less inviting region. A storm was brewing and the light rapidly failing, making it impossible to take a photograph, though no photograph could produce a picture that would give an adequate idea of the savage grandeur of the whole scene. It was indeed sufficient to awe and terrorise one. Such scenes sink deep into the memory and the impressive stillness produces an effect which is felt for long years afterwards.[6]

Top: A view of the north gate of the city of Daning, on the Daning River, eastern Sichuan.

Bottom: These irrigation wheels seen near Daning were propelled by the current of the river. Paddles made from bamboo matting carried water to the trough near the top of the wheel. From there a system of bamboo pipes took the water to the fields.

The first important city they would reach on the way to Chengdu was Xuanhan. The route lay via a difficult descent to the village seen from Hsao-Pingtsze, and then 9 miles by native boat along the Daning River to Daning. Daning was ten days' march from Xuanhan, and the almost unbearably hot weather made the journey exhausting. Accommodation was poor, and Wilson's men were suffering from stomach troubles and sores. Everyone was feeling worn out and irritable, as Wilson's journal entry for 5 July 1910 shows:

We lunched at the village of Kao-chiao, and a more hot, fly-infested, stinking hole, with people more inquisitive, I have not experienced. Savage, yelping dogs abounded, and these, with other discomforts did not add to the relish of the meal. My followers seemed to share my views of this village, and grumbling and malediction were loud on all sides. Our meal did not occupy long, and we all felt better when clear of this filthy pestiferous place.

The last leg of the journey was a little easier. Travelling by boat from a place he called Nan-pa ch'ang, they reached Xuanhan in eight hours. Here Wilson was able to relax a little. There was a Roman Catholic Mission in the city, and he spent some time in the company of an Irish missionary, the first European he had met since he left Yichang, thirty-five days earlier.

It had been a gruelling time for Wilson and his men, but the flora had been rich. He collected more than thirty different kinds of woody plant, including the new lilac mentioned above, two previously unknown species of beech and a new *Stachyurus*. One of his most pleasing finds was a most unusual hydrangea, *H. sargentiana*. From a collecting standpoint, the trip had been very worth while.

Rice cultivation in the rich red basin of north central Sichuan. Note the terraces cut into the hillside.

Once he had reached Xuanhan, Wilson had to decide on a route for the next section of the expedition, due west to Langzhong (then known as Paoning). The information available for route planning was of two kinds: firsthand information from local inhabitants obtained through an interpreter, and the official maps drawn up by the British army over the previous half-century. The former often proved unreliable, the latter inaccurate. His War Office map, 'Province of Ssu-ch'uan, Eastern Sheet', did not show a route but indicated a number of scattered hamlets. Wilson deduced that these centres of population must be connected by some sort of road. Though the going would be much harder, he would certainly be breaking new ground, and he reasoned that his chances of discovering new plants were likely to be greater. After many inquiries in Xuanhan, he was able to confirm that a route of sorts did exist but that he could expect only the crudest of tracks and the most primitive of hostels.

Undaunted by this information, he set off on the morning of 8 July accompanied by his usual men, a few extra hands and two armed soldiers. These last were provided by the local magistrate as protection against attack by bandits, who were known to be operating in that area. The destination for this first day was a village he called Shuang-miao ch'ang, but on arrival they found a market in progress, and Wilson decided to press on. Instead they put up at a farmhouse situated a mile or so from the village.

Arriving at a village on market day was something to be avoided wherever possible; not only was it difficult to find accommodation, but the caravan would attract unwelcome attention from what Wilson called the 'idlers and loafers' who

Market villages like this one, near Langzhong, usually consisted of a single street almost entirely covered in by the eaves of the houses.

'CHINESE' WILSON

frequented such places. At one such village, the last before they reached Chengdu, he describes how 'a mob rushed our inn and bedlam reigned for a couple of hours. Eventually it thinned down, but many of the more insistent and curious remained until bedtime.'[7] In this part of Sichuan, however, the villages were only about 10 miles apart and each held a market nine days a month, so it was hard to avoid them.

Even stopping outside villages did not always mean that the party escaped the curiosity of the local inhabitants. Wilson described how one place where they stayed was surrounded by 'a constant crowd until after dark when the doors were closed. We found all these crowds quiet and orderly enough, but a continuous mass of faces, with wooden expressions, blocking the doorway, obstructing light and air, is very trying.'[8] On 18 July, ten days after leaving Xuanhan, the party arrived at Langzhong. This was a walled city, with many fine buildings, but Wilson describes it as a place of 'past rather than present greatness'. Once the centre of a thriving silk industry, it was now suffering a period of decline. Trading was confined to a single street and the most noteworthy items for sale were umbrellas and vinegar. (Apparently Langzhong was famous for its vinegar, which was very good quality.) The city was also an important missionary centre and the seat of a Protestant bishopric, and Wilson had time to meet the bishop and his assistants briefly before continuing his journey.

They travelled the rest of the way to Chengdu along the main road in easy stages and reached the city on 27 July. Wilson was now in familiar territory, having visited Chengdu and the surrounding area both on his second expedition for the Veitches and on his previous journey for the Arnold Arboretum. This time he

Another small settlement near Langzhong. Some fine Chinese buildings can be seen in this photograph, and in the foreground is one of Wilson's chairs.

decided to revisit the border town of Songpan, travelling first to An Xian, north of Chengdu, and then along a difficult mountain route few Europeans had used. In the area around Songpan he hoped to find seeds and other specimens of new conifers.

The journey from An Xian did not begin well. One day out of the town it was discovered that one of the bearers had absconded and taken with him some of the expedition's silver. The sum taken was considerable: 30 taels and 5 Szechwan dollars.[9] Wilson took the loss philosophically. He reasoned that his chances of catching up with the man were slim and that any involvement with Chinese magistrates would only cause lengthy delay to the expedition. Writing about this incident later, he pointed out that the culprit had left about half the amount contained in the box and that since he had about three-quarters of a day's start on them, there was no point in pursuing the matter. 'I concluded it was best to quietly cut the loss, my first and last in China,' he wrote.[10] Wilson's attitude seems to have been very different in this respect from some of his plant hunting contemporaries, Frank Kingdon Ward, for example, who seems to have been prepared to have had Chinese villagers beaten for the theft of a Thermos flask.[11]

A further four days' march across rough mountainous territory brought the expedition to a point from which it was possible to join the Pingwu highway to Songpan.

The beauty of the countryside and the lushness of the vegetation along the route contrasted strongly with the poverty of the Chinese peasants who lived there.

Bottom left: The 'Great Salt Road' was a demanding route. At one point the road passed through this natural tunnel.

Bottom right: A view of the countryside south-east of Songpan.

'CHINESE' WILSON

Most of the houses he passed were dilapidated and the accommodation Wilson and his men were able to find provided little in the way of comforts. However, the weather was fine and Wilson describes the scenery as magnificent.

On 20 August the caravan came within sight of Songpan. As before, Wilson was impressed by its prosperity and its idyllic setting:

nestling in a narrow, smiling valley, surrounded on all sides by fields of golden grain, with the infant Min, a clear, limpid stream, winding its way through in a series of graceful curves. In the fields the harvesters were busy, men, women and children, mostly tribesfolk, in quaint costume, all pictures of rude health, laughing and singing at their work.[12]

The expedition spent several days here resting and obtaining fresh provisions. Leaving on or about 25 August, Wilson and his men began the difficult descent of the Min gorge. The chief task for this trip was to locate and record the habitat of the regal lily, which Wilson had so far failed to introduce successfully to the West.

For seven days they followed the Min River as it cut its way through the mountainous countryside. The weather was unbearably hot and the route was rock-strewn and extremely fatiguing to travel. Here and there the track had been blasted from the solid rock and notices carved into the stone warned of the dangers of rock falls.

On the seventh day Wilson made this entry in his diary:

A bad road through barren, desolate country and abnormally long miles sums up the day's journey. Barring absolute desert no more barren and repelling country could be imagined

The city of Songpan from the east. The prosperity of this place contrasted greatly with the poverty Wilson had seen in the surrounding countryside.

than that traversed today. But it is really only the narrow valley and precipitous mountain-sides that are so desert like. On the upper slopes trees and cultivation occur and small villages and farmhouses are frequent. In the valley houses are far between and what few there are are in ruinous condition. A fierce up-river wind blows regularly from about eleven o'clock in the morning and it is difficult to make headway against it. The leaves on the Maize plants are torn to shreds by the wind's violence. The houses are of mud and flat-roofed, as a protection against the winds. The Regal Lily occurs here and there in abundance on the well nigh stark slate and mudstone cliffs.[13]

The expedition camped out on the eighth day and spent several days marking the position of some six or seven thousand lily plants. *Lilium regale* was in flower throughout the hot summer months but on dying down disappeared without trace. Wilson's collectors would return that October to lift the bulbs from the locations he had marked.

On the morning of 3 September the expedition broke camp and set off on the return journey to Chengdu. By this time Wilson was beginning to show signs of fatigue, and his journal entry for that day reads: 'I am certainly getting very tired of the wandering life and long for the end to come. I seem never to have done anything else than wander, wander – through China.'

Now that Chengdu was only four days' march away, the whole party was in cheerful mood, however. The caravan was making good progress and Wilson was taking his ease in his chair. His black spaniel ran a little way ahead of the column as they negotiated a narrow mountain track:

A view of some of the desolate countryside beyond Songpan. A ruined fort stands in the foreground and the forbidding mountain ranges in the distance are topped by eternal snows.

'CHINESE' WILSON

Song was in our hearts, when I noticed my dog suddenly cease wagging his tail, cringe and rush forward and a small piece of rock hit the path and rebounded into the river some 300 feet below us. I shouted an order and the bearers put down the chair. The two front bearers ran forward and I essayed to follow suit. Just as I cleared the chair handles a large boulder crashed into the body of the chair and down to the river it was hurled. I ran, instinctively ducked as something whisked over my head and my sun hat blew off. Again I ran, a few yards more and I would be under the lea of some hard rocks. Then feeling as if a hot wire passed through my leg, I was bowled over, tried to jump up, found my right leg was useless, so crawled forward to the shelter of the cliff, where the two scared chair-bearers were huddled.[14]

Looking down at his right leg, Wilson saw that the pigskin puttee had been forced round and slashed as if with a knife. The toe-cap of his right boot had been torn off along with the nail of his big toe. The leg was broken in two places and his flesh badly lacerated. He was now in considerable pain but he managed to remain conscious.

Wilson gave orders for the heavy camera tripod to be lashed to his injured leg as a makeshift splint, while his Boy supervised the retrieval of his chair from the ravine. Just as these tasks were being completed, a caravan of mules came along the narrow track.

According to those who knew him in private life, Wilson was always modest about his work. 'He disliked heroics', wrote his friend and biographer Edward Farrington, 'That is why so little is known about his adventures in the Far East. Even his books no more than suggest the dangers which he encountered and the narrow escapes from death which were his.'[15] Sometimes, however, Wilson would describe some of his experiences in a humorous way. This is what he did when he described this incident in *Plant Hunting*: 'How many people know the size of a mule's hoof? Quite a number have felt the strength of a mule's leg and the sharpness of his teeth; his obstinacy is a proverb. But the size of his hoof is another matter.'[16]

The track was very narrow and the mules could neither turn around nor back up. There was only one solution to this predicament. Wilson was laid across the roadway and the mules urged gently forward: 'I lay across the road and the mules stepped over my body. Then it was that I realized the size of the mule's hoof. There were nearer fifty than forty of them and each stepped clearly over me as if accustomed to such obstacles. Nevertheless, I breathed freely when the last was over!'[17]

It was now a matter of life and death to return as speedily as possibly to Chengdu. The leg was very badly injured and it was imperative for it to receive medical attention before infection set in. Marching both early and late they reached the city in just three days, arriving on 6 September. Wilson was taken immediately to the house of a doctor from the Friends' Mission.

In spite of all their efforts, the leg was badly infected and the bones had still not healed six weeks later. For a time it looked as though amputation might be necessary, but with some 'cutting' and 'draining' the infection was finally halted. It was to be another three months, however, before he could walk, hobbling on crutches. He had been in considerable pain for much of this time, but he bore it well. Wilson was proving to be as hardy as many of his plant introductions.

Wilson had written to Sargent just a week after his accident. Typically his primary concern had been for the well-being of the expedition: 'Fortunately, as far as the expedition is concerned my plans have been so laid that, whilst handicapping us, the accident cannot involve the expedition in entire failure'.[18] He added a post-script to the effect that news of his ill fortune should not be allowed to reach

A main street in Chengdu in 1910. Wilson had visited this city during both his previous expeditions to China, and knew it well.

his wife and that he would inform her himself once he was well on the way to making a full recovery. That time was likely to be several months away and Wilson could see that no useful purpose would be served by worrying Nellie now with news of his misadventure.

During Wilson's enforced absence from the field his faithful collectors did all that they could to gather the required seed and other plant material. Many of his men by this time were very experienced in this work and their efforts resulted in a good harvest. The regal lily bulbs were also successfully dug up, encased in clay and shipped in good condition to Boston.

On 4 December 1910, Wilson again wrote to Sargent. The leg was healing badly and he was in considerable pain and discomfort. 'They [the doctors] advise me on reaching civilization to have the limb re-broken and re-set. I have suffered so much that I do not know whether I shall have the necessary courage to undergo another operation.'[19] Wilson had needed much remedial attention after gangrene had appeared in the leg and the surgery had been as much as he felt he could endure. 'I had had enough of chloroform and the last operation was done under a heavy dose of morphia and a strong local anaesthetic. I did not feel the cutting very much but the dressing afterwards was nearly the "limit".'[20]

Wilson also wrote to Colonel Prain, Thiselton-Dyer's successor at Kew, of the success of the second Harvard expedition:

We have luckily caught the conifers seeding freely and have secured a good haul of the seed of at least four-fifths of the species known to exist in these regions. I have got all the Abies [firs], including two species not collected on my last journey and at least one entirely new species. In all I have some thirty-six numbers of conifer seeds. Of seeds of trees and shrubs generally I have done very well. The same is true of lily-bulbs and young plants of willows, poplars etc.[21]

In December Wilson made plans for his return home. He travelled first to Shanghai and from there sailed for the United States via Vancouver, arriving in Boston in March 1911.

In his last letter to Sargent from China, dated 28 January 1911, he sums up his ill-fated fourth expedition:

The accident has put an end to my travels and rendered me a bit of a cripple to the end of my days, but I have been able to wind up my work successfully and in consequence I have no vain regrets. I have enjoyed my work in China and am proud in the knowledge that I have been privileged to achieve success in worthy employ and am certainly not going to pull a long face because the Fates have unkindly given me a parting kick.[22]

Wilson was undoubtedly a fatalist by nature. He had first gone to China as a young botanist, completely unknown. Now, at the age of thirty-four, he had a world-wide reputation. China had been good to Wilson and he was certainly not going to carp at the way she had treated him at the last.

After his accident, Wilson was treated by Dr Davidson at the Friends' Mission in Chengdu. This photograph shows the Davidsons' home in the mission compound. Dr Davidson and his wife are standing on the veranda.

In Boston, Wilson spent a few more weeks in hospital. His right leg had healed but it was crooked and now nearly an inch shorter than his left. However, with the aid of a special boot he was soon able to walk with a cane, though he suffered the remaining twenty years of his life from what he called his 'lily limp'.

The bulbs of the regal lily arrived safely in Boston and were planted out in a field in Roslindale, Massachusetts, where they flowered freely the following June. This lily was a great success and Wilson was extremely proud of having discovered it and given it its name.[23] Though it had cost him dear to bring it to the gardens of the West, he always felt that it had been well worth the price he had paid, and it would always be his favourite introduction.

Wilson selected fifty of the Japanese dwarf hybrid azaleas (known as the 'Kurume azaleas') that he saw in Japan for introduction to the United States. This one, 'Kureno-yuki' was photographed in the garden of the Japanese grower Kijiro Akashi.

Chapter Five
Japan, Korea and Taiwan

Once more on his feet, albeit with the assistance of a cane, Wilson returned to his wife and daughter in England. He spent three months there recuperating and having remedial treatment to his injured leg before returning with his family to Boston.

In 1910 he had been offered the post of superintendent of the Botany and Forestry Department in Hong Kong 'at the maximum salary to commence'. Wilson, however, decided not to accept the appointment.[1] To reject such a prestigious position, he must have been fairly certain of his standing with the Arnold Arboretum. On his return from China he had been astonished to find himself something of a celebrity. News of his accident and near scrape with death had captured the imagination of the Boston press, whose reporters pursued him eagerly for stories of his exploits. This was when the name 'Chinese' Wilson was coined, the name that would remain with him for the rest of his life and make him a legend in the world of horticulture.

No doubt Sargent was more than pleased with Wilson's rise to fame, and he must have viewed the publication of his adventures as something which could only be good for the Arboretum. He encouraged him to write popular articles about his travels for various gardening publications as well as contributing to the Arboretum's own journal, and Wilson also gave lectures and, at the height of his fame, radio talks. He was particularly keen to popularise gardening as a hobby in the United States, and it seems that his lectures and many of his books were written with this in mind. In addition to his salary, Wilson could now look forward to receiving regular fees for his published articles and lectures, and the family set up home in a modest apartment near the Arboretum.

In 1911 he began work on a catalogue of his Chinese collections. The project had been Sargent's idea, and Sargent was to act as editor. For this work Wilson co-operated with another member of the Arboretum's staff, Alfred Rehder, who in fact was to make the greater contribution to the work. Altogether, Wilson's collections from the Arboretum's two expeditions to China amounted to a staggering 65,000 specimens, representing 4700 plant species. In addition there were 1593 lots of seed and 168 lots of plant cuttings. It was to be six years before the last of the three volumes of *Plantae Wilsonianae* was ready for publication. It would seem that Wilson did not regard this work with quite the same enthusiasm as Sargent or Rehder. Taxonomy was not his forte and Rehder assumed responsibility for most of the classification work.[2]

Towards the end of 1911 Wilson began work on a book of his own, a task that was to occupy most of his spare time for the next two years. This book, *A Naturalist in Western China*, was his first and arguably his finest. He clearly much enjoyed writing it:

All my spare time for more than a year now has been occupied in writing a book on China and it is this task that has been the cause of my letters being so few and far between. The hardest part of the work is now finished and I hope to enjoy more leisure. However, I like work and should be miserable had I not plenty to do. Luckily there is small chance of my ever being idle. The work I have devoted my life to is very engrossing and will afford me amusement and employment if nothing else, for the rest of my days. However I shall be able to say in all humbleness and truth that I have accomplished something for having lived. This is sufficient reward.[3]

He was much more content than he had been at the beginning of 1910. Now that his days of exploration were at an end, he had found a new interest – and, perhaps, a second career – as a writer. As his income had improved, moreover, life in America had more appeal for him. News from England of the coal strike of 1912 and the suffering that this had brought perhaps dampened his enthusiasm for an early return.

In 1912 Wilson was awarded the Victoria Medal of Honour by the Royal Horticultural Society for his services to horticulture.[4] Many more honours were to follow, and he received nearly a hundred awards for his work during his lifetime. Yet he was modest about his achievements. In Kipling's words, he was a man who could 'meet with Triumph and Disaster' and treat them 'just the same'.

He did take great pleasure in the success of his writings, however. *A Naturalist in Western China* was published in two volumes in November 1913, and he wrote to his mother:

I am happy to say that the book is being most favourably received by the English public. Every mail brings me letters of congratulation from friends and acquaintances and there is good reason to believe that it will enjoy a successful sale. There is, however, very little money to be made from such books but I felt that its publication was a duty owed to myself and to the science to which I have devoted my life. I got considerable amusement from writing it and much satisfaction from its appearance when issued. The American edition is sent out tomorrow and it will be interesting to watch its reception among my yankee friends.[5]

The book is a very readable account of his exploits in China. Drawing heavily on his notebooks and diaries, he gives the reader a vivid picture of China in the decade before the revolution. Oddly, the book is not written chronologically (it contains very few dates) and some chapters contain exploits from more than one expedition. It is worth noting that *China, Mother of Gardens*, which was published in one volume in 1929, repeats much of the material in *A Naturalist in Western China*, with whole chapters reproduced verbatim.

Towards the end of 1913 Sargent approached Wilson with a plan for a new expedition for the Arboretum. It was now more than two years since his accident and though his leg still gave him some discomfort it was now quite strong. Though another tough expedition in China was out of the question, Sargent felt that the Arboretum could get better value in return for Wilson's salary if he were once more in the field. The plan was for Wilson to spend a year or so in Japan studying plants in cultivation there. As this would not be the test of endurance that his other trips had proved to be, Wilson decided to take his family along with him.

The Wilsons left the United States for Japan on 1 January 1914. Just before sailing Wilson wrote to his mother that this trip would be 'one long holiday for me

Wilson's mother at about the time of the First World War.

and a complete change for Nellie. I have worked pretty hard since I have been over here and can do with a rest and a change. Nellie feels the same way.'[6]

After a rough and stormy voyage across the Pacific, they arrived in Japan on 3 February. Wilson's plan was to make Tokyo his base, from where he could arrange various trips up and down the islands of Japan. He installed his family at the Imperial Hotel, where they would remain until the summer. Nellie and Muriel would then move up into the mountains, where it was cooler. 'Everything is novel and interesting', he wrote to his mother, 'especially to Nellie and Muriel and both are having the time of their lives. Having them with me makes it much pleasanter and infinitely less lonely for me.'[7]

Wilson spent much of February and March in southern Japan, where he made a special study of Japanese cherries.[8] In one garden he noted eighty different forms. From this single location he collected herbarium specimens of sixty-three named varieties. In April and the first half of June he collected in central Japan. His family had by this time moved up into the mountains and were now staying in Nikko, 60 miles north of Tokyo.

Communications within Japan were very different from those in China, and Wilson made full use of the railway network that operated over the whole length of

Bottom left: a studio portrait of Ernest, Nellie and Muriel, taken in about 1914, probably in Tokyo.

Bottom right: Wilson's photographs could be sensitive as well as accomplished, as in this study of Muriel, taken in Japan.

'CHINESE' WILSON

the country. In this way he was able to cover large tracts of countryside rapidly and in comparative comfort.

This expedition was turning out to be every bit as pleasant as he had forecast. Nellie and Muriel both seemed to be enjoying the visit and they were all intending to return to the United States in 1915 via England. However, events in Europe were to alter these plans, and cast a shadow over what felt like a holiday.

He was half-way through a trip to the north of Japan when news of the outbreak of a European war reached him. His next letter to his mother combined reassurance about the situation in Japan with horror at what was happening in Europe:

Since you wrote this terrible war has broken out and half the world is face to face with ruin. Here, although Japan is at war with Germany, everything is quiet and orderly. All foreigners enjoy perfect safety and we come and go as formerly. The people are as polite and courteous as ever and but for the newspapers there is nothing to indicate that terrible war is raging through the world. If you have any misgivings for our safety please dismiss them from your mind for good and all. We are just as safe as you and nothing can happen to alter this situation. The allies are bound to win in good time and the world will be all the better for

Travelling in Japan was far easier and more comfortable than travelling in China. Wilson was able to move about the countryside rapidly using the extensive railway network.

having got rid of German military aggression. It is however dreadful to realise that the blood-thirstyness of the German Kaiser should cause such an awful waste of human lives and money. Would that he and his alone should pay the price of his abominable madness.[9]

It would appear that Wilson was not taken up with the patriotic fervour of the time. He was saddened by the conflict and realised even in the war's early stages that victory would be hard won and costly. As the casualty lists grew, however, his inability to play an active role troubled him greatly, and he cursed the fact that his crippled leg prevented him from fighting for his country.

In the autumn of 1914 Wilson returned to central Japan and in November and December of that year collected on the island of Shikoku. His year-long expedition had turned out to be a very worthwhile enterprise. Altogether he had amassed a collection of some 2000 specimens and he had taken about 600 photographs. One of the principal aims of the expedition had been for Wilson to catalogue the conifers and taxads (yews) found in Japan, and it seems that he managed to see almost every conifer and yew known there growing in the wild. He was clearly proud of this accomplishment: 'There is no record of anyone – foreigner or native – having previously enjoyed such an opportunity to study these plants,' he wrote.[10]

At the beginning of January 1915 he was ready to return to the United States. The shores around Britain were becoming ever more dangerous, and a visit to England was now out of the question. Wilson and his family sailed direct to San Francisco and by the end of January 1915 they were once more back in Boston.

Wilson with a group of Japanese forestry officials in 1914.

Wilson's anxiety about the war continued after his return. The Americans around him could afford to be detached (a letter of Sargent's penned within days of the sinking of the *Lusitania* and commenting 'Pretty bad times these but there is no use thinking about them when there are trees to think of'[11] is perhaps not untypical), but it was a very different matter for an Englishman. In July 1915 he wrote to his mother:

This war hangs like a horrid nightmare over the world and one thinks of nothing else. I greedily devour my two newspapers each day and this and work occupies my whole time. One has little heart for letter writing and you never know if they will reach their destination. The end will come sometime but it is certainly a long long way to go.[12]

His principal task for that year was to continue with the mammoth catalogue of his Chinese introductions, *Plantae Wilsonianae*. Co-author for this work was Alfred Rehder, with whom Wilson had enjoyed an amicable working relationship. Indeed the two men and their families had something of a social life together. Rehder, however, was a German-American with strong pro-German loyalties, and their relationship was bound to deteriorate.

The mail from England contained depressing news of shortages of food and coal, but Wilson did not always respond sympathetically to his family's complaints. 'I fear this will be a hard winter for the poor' he wrote to his mother, 'but it is no use complaining, money must be found to carry on the war to a successful end and rich and poor alike must make sacrifices.'[13]

Wilson's restlessness was not lost on Sargent and in an effort to divert his attention from the war he encouraged him to prepare two monographs for the Arnold Arboretum on the discoveries he had made on his last expedition. *The Cherries of Japan* and *The Conifers and Taxads of Japan* were published in 1916.

In 1915 Wilson was awarded the George Robert White Medal of Honor by the Massachusetts Horticultural Society for his 'eminent service in Horticulture'.[14] The following year the University of Harvard granted him an honorary Master of Arts degree for his work. It is hard to believe that until this time Wilson had very little in the way of academic qualifications. From his time at Kew at the end of the previous century to his permanent employment at the Arnold Arboretum he had never been settled anywhere long enough to complete a degree course.

In fact Wilson never did settle for life as an academic. He grew to love the Arnold Arboretum as a substitute for his 'beloved Kew' and he much enjoyed his writing; but he was principally a man of action, who thrived on physical challenge. Fieldwork was his real forte and Sargent recognised this. Sargent therefore proposed that Wilson should return once more to the Far East. In addition to making further investigations in Japan he would journey to Korea and the island of Taiwan, where earlier expeditions had revealed plant species quite distinct from the flora of the Japanese islands.

It was suggested that whilst in Japan Wilson should make every effort to secure living plants of a selection of the dwarf azaleas that he had been shown in 1914. At that time Wilson had only been able to obtain dried specimens, but these had indicated sufficient merit to make their introduction worthwhile. For these plants Wilson would travel to the city of Kurume, their place of origin.

By now Wilson was of sufficient value to the Arboretum to be able to make his own terms for such an expedition. His previous trip to Japan with his family had been a success and he insisted that his wife and daughter should again accompany him. The travel arrangements and accommodation would of course be 'first class'.

The Wilsons sailed from San Francisco in January 1917 aboard the Japanese steamer *Siberia Maru* and they arrived in Yokohama in the middle of February. They then travelled on to Tokyo, where Nellie and Muriel would remain during the plant hunter's expeditions up and down the country. Wilson installed his family at a hotel and engaged a Japanese companion to look after them during his absence. Each of his trips would occupy two or three weeks at a time.

Having completed his family's domestic arrangements, Wilson set off for the Ryukyu Islands, in the East China Sea between Japan and Taiwan. After a rather rough passage he arrived at the main island, Okinawa. He spent seventeen days exploring the flora there and also found time to visit several of the outlying islets:

A fruit and vegetable market in Japan. Wilson can be seen second left, and his 'faithful and most efficient Japanese "Boy", Morita' is second to the right.

The northern part of the island [Okinawa] is mountainous and sparsely populated and is partly of coral rock and partly volcanic . . . Near the sea the flora is composed mainly of subtropical and tropical plants which have a wide distribution in the tropics . . . The Liukiu people are a distinct race, probably of Malay origin, in the main part farmers, part fishermen. The manners and customs are peculiar and very different from those of China and Japan. As a race they are smaller folk than the Japanese and their manners are mild and inoffensive. The women in particular work very hard and carry all loads on their heads. Children abound and seem happy, carefree mites. The houses are very small, of bamboo wattle sides and thatched roofs and each is enclosed by a wall or fence. The people seem very poor and whatever wealth they amass appears to be squandered on the construction of enormous family tombs. By education of the children and the development of various industries the Japanese are doing much toward the improvement of the conditions and social life of the Liukiu people.[15]

On these islands Wilson collected over 600 specimens representing more than 100 species: 'Of the more interesting plants collected I may mention *Quercus Miyagii, Buxus liukiuensis, Tournefortia argentea, Myoporum botioides, Rhododendron Tashiroi, R. sublanceolatum*, two palms, three Mangroves and a local variety of loose-skinned Orange, said to be indigenous and known as "Tachibana". The *R. sublanceolatum* is the sole representative in Liukiu of the group loosely called *R. indicum* in books, and is endemic.'[16] Wilson also took time to make a photographic record of his visit. Using his large plate camera he took some five dozen photographs.

In April and the first half of May he investigated the flora of the Bonin Islands, to the south of Japan, and made a particular study of the woody plants to be found there.[17] He was also to discover a group of people living on these islands who conversed in English. They were apparently the descendants of American seamen who had migrated there a hundred years previously from Salem, Massachusetts.

Despite these absorbing diversions he was still very preoccupied with the war in Europe, and concerned about his family in England. Trade was slow, and they were obviously having trouble making ends meet. He wrote to them sternly, however:

This War pinches all of us – some more than others – but it is useless and foolish to complain. The War must continue until Germany is thoroughly beaten or all sacrifices will have been in vain. Did Germany win remember she would treat England worse if possible than she has done Belgium. We all want the War to end and end as speedily as possible but we want it to end right so that our future is safe.[18]

He could see that there would be no early end to the war and that people in England would be making sacrifices for a long time to come. To ease his family's hardship a little, he increased the amount of money he sent home each month by £1.

Also in this letter he reveals something of the frustration he was feeling at his inability to take part in the fighting: 'I am glad to learn that Brother Dick has joined

Opposite: Wilson in Korea in 1917. Despite his injured leg, he was still able to undertake extensive field-work on foot.

the Army and though it is natural for you to miss him you should not worry. He is only doing his duty as an Englishman. But for my leg I should have been in it long ago.'

In mid-May 1917 Wilson journeyed to Korea and the following month he had Nellie and Muriel join him in Seoul. The climate here in the summer months was much healthier than that of Tokyo, and Muriel would be able to attend the school which had been established for the children of the British Consular Service.

Since the annexation of Korea by Japan in 1910, there had been a systematic cataloguing of the country's natural resources, including its flora. This last task had fallen largely to Dr T Nakai, the Japanese government's botanist in Korea. Nakai had been able to identify 3000 species of plants, representing some 800 genera. Generally the flora was similar to that of Japan and northern China but not as rich. There had been several valuable plant discoveries here in the early 1900s, including the 'clove-scented' *Viburnum carlesii*, which was introduced to the West by way of Japan in 1902.

Using Seoul as his base, Wilson was able to use the rail network to travel the length of Korea, much as he had done in Japan. He found that large-scale deforestation had taken place and that only a few of the mountainous areas (the Diamond Mountains in particular) had retained their forests intact. He therefore spent considerable time exploring these. 'Not even in the richest parts of China or Japan' he wrote 'have I seen such extensive displays of pure pink and white as on the Diamond Mountains, where *Rhododendron Schlippenbachii* and *Magnolia parviflora* dominate the undergrowth for miles and bloom to perfection.'[19]

In addition to exploring the countryside of Korea, Wilson made several short excursions to the island of Dagalet, now known as Ullung-do, 100 miles off the coast of Korea, in the Sea of Japan. For some of these trips Wilson was fortunate to have the company of Dr Nakai, whose knowledge would have been invaluable to the English botanist. The flora of these islands is described by Wilson as 'singular' and probably more closely related to that of Japan than Korea.

The remaining months of 1917 were spent by Wilson in further exploring the Korean mainland and in November of that year, the island now known as Cheju,[20] off the south coast of Korea. On this island he was to find that the most characteristic varieties of plant were broad-leaved evergreens, including several not to be found on mainland Korea.

The eight-month expedition to Korea had been made up of a number of short trips of two or three weeks' duration. Between trips he would return to the hotel in Seoul where his family were staying. In the New Year, Wilson determined on a less leisurely expedition to the island of Taiwan by way of the Japanese mainland.

In 1918, Taiwan (then Formosa) was part of the Japanese empire. The population was a mixture of Japanese, Chinese who had migrated from the mainland, and the aboriginal inhabitants of the island. The latter, who Wilson refers

JAPAN, KOREA AND TAIWAN

to as 'the savages', were much feared on account of their reputation for head-hunting. Although this mainly seems to have taken place in the course of inter-tribal warfare, there had been incidents involving foreigners, and punitive expeditions had been mounted which had greatly reduced their numbers. When Wilson visited Taiwan, the tribes were under the strict control of the Japanese police service: 'Roads have been built, block-houses installed and a large police patrol placed in charge. The more irreconcilable tribes are segregated and surrounded by wire fences charged with heavy electric voltage.'[21] Although he employed some of these people as porters on his expeditions in Taiwan (accompanied by armed Japanese policemen), he could never regard them as harmless.

Wilson's main aim in visiting Taiwan was to investigate the forests there and to secure seeds and living plants of cone-bearing trees. The island was known to have a great many giant trees, some of which were thought to rival the sequoias and yellow cedars of western North America. One tree in which he was particularly interested was the taiwania, *Taiwania cryptomerioides*, which could grow as tall as 150–200 ft and attain a girth of as much as 30 ft. In youth the tree was quite beautiful, but on maturity it lost its lower foliage and would eventually become completely denuded except for a bushy topknot. It took him several months of searching to find a mature specimen of this tree from which he could obtain a good haul of seed. Several hundred plants were later grown from the seeds he sent to the Arnold Arboretum, and these were distributed world-wide.

Bottom left: Dr T Nakai, the Japanese government's botanist in Korea, accompanied Wilson on several expeditions. His knowledge proved invaluable to the English plant hunter.

Bottom right: One of the main objects of Wilson's expedition to Taiwan was to secure seed of the taiwania, *Taiwania cryptomerioides*. A good example of this tree may be seen in the Temperate House at the Royal Botanic Gardens, Kew.

88

The largest tree examined by Wilson on Taiwan was the white cedar, *Chamaecyparis formosensis*. Examples he measured there had heights approaching 200 ft and girths as large as 64 ft. These trees were very ancient and after examining the rings of a felled specimen Wilson was able to put their ages at something in excess of 2500 years.

The Japanese government had co-operated completely with Wilson's expedition. Two of their best forestry officials, Messrs Kanehira and Sasaki, were detailed to give him every assistance. Wilson was also granted permission to use the Japanese-built steam railway between the west coast and the central mountains.

Wilson assembled his caravan at a place he called Arisan in the central mountains in late February 1918:

Like many other unsophisticated people, the Formosan savage is not partial to manual labor, neither is money an over-weening incentive to work. A bribe of Chinese wine is much more potent but even this is not always sufficient. Being a born hunter of game as well as human heads, the savage dearly loves a gun and to be allowed to carry a rifle with a nice shining barrel, to aim it, pull back the breech and kill as his imagination wills, is irresistible. So pleasing his fancy in this matter, but allowing him dummy cartridges only, and adding a goodly number of kerosene tins filled with Chinese wine, we had little difficulty in securing some two score savages as porters.[22]

The rest of the party was made up of a squad of armed Japanese policemen,

Plant hunting in Taiwan. Here Wilson's caravan included a party of 'reformed head-hunters', who acted as porters, and a number of armed policemen for Wilson's protection.

Wilson's 'faithful and most efficient Japanese boy, Morita', Kanehira, Sasaki and Wilson himself.

Plant Hunting includes an atmospheric description of the expedition's first night out in the forest:

'Well, if they take a fancy for my head during the night I do not see what is to prevent them from taking it'. With this lugubrious soliloquy, I rolled myself in a blanket and prepared for sleep beneath the shelter of a fallen tree. A recent storm had blown down one of the giants of the forest and there was plenty of room for a dozen people in the cavern beneath its base. Some pieces of old tent canvas strung across the front shielded us from without and the clayey earth adhering to the roots of the tree formed a roof. Gathered around several fires were two score half-naked ex-head-hunters, armed with bows and arrows, long knives and guns, who had struggled all day up the mountain slope carrying our belongings. It was a weird scene in the heart of the mountains of Formosa. The night was fine but dark with a darkness that could almost be felt. The savages had finished their frugal meal washed down with the crude Chinese wine of which they are fond. Some were smoking and sharpening their knives, others were pleasantly crooning songs of the chase. As I lay on the ground this scene of savages grouped around camp-fires, in the light of whose flames their faces showed clearly through rents in the canvas, the gloom and mystery of the forest immediately beyond, brought forth my soliloquy and became indelibly written on my memory. It had been a hard day's tramp and soon my Japanese companions and self were sound asleep.[23]

In April 1918 Wilson left Taiwan and returned to Japan. Four years previously he had been shown a selection of dwarf azaleas at a nursery a few miles north of Tokyo. Now it was his intention to visit the city of Kurume on the island of Kyushu, where these plants had first been raised by an early 19th-century nurseryman, Motozo Sakamoto. On his first visit to the Far East Wilson had observed that much of Japan's culture had been borrowed from her ancient neighbour, China. He found, however, that the Japanese love of flowers was more highly developed than that of the Chinese and that Japan enjoyed a tradition in horticultural science which spanned many centuries. The skill and knowledge of Japanese nurserymen was acknowledged throughout the world of horticulture.

Wilson arrived at Kurume in May and went straight away to visit the nursery of Mr Kijiro Akashi, to whom the stock of azaleas had passed on the death of Sakamoto. Akashi himself had devoted forty years of his own life developing the range of these dwarf hybrids and he had some 250 at the time of Wilson's visit. Wilson selected what he felt were the 'fifty best' for introducing to the United States. He informs us in *Plant Hunting* that making a selection proved to be much easier than persuading Akashi to part with them. He names six as being the pick of them all: 'Takasago' ('Cherryblossom') – cherry blossom pink; 'Azuma Kagami' ('Pink Pearl') – deep pink; 'Kirin' ('Daybreak') – deep rose; 'Kumo-no-uye' ('Salmon Prince') – pure salmon; 'Kurai-no-himo' ('Carmine Queen') – carmine; and 'Kureno-yuki' ('Snowflake') – white.

On leaving Kurume, Wilson travelled to the south of Japan to visit the sacred mountain of Kirishima. It was from here, he had been told, that the parent stock obtained by Sakamoto had come. On this mountain, at an altitude of 3000 ft, he found the slopes covered with azaleas in full flower – pink, salmon, mauve and magenta. Higher up he found pure red and white forms. He had little doubt that this was indeed the place where the parents of the Kurume azaleas had originated.

Wilson was extremely proud of introducing these plants to America, and *Plant Hunting* describes them in glowing terms. In the chapter entitled 'The Princess Kurume', his delight is expressed in an uncharacteristically artificial style:

We have the honor to announce that Princess Kurume, reigning beauty of the Azalea Kingdom, is in town and will hold court throughout Easter. Further, I have to declare the Princess' intention of becoming a permanent resident, also, that in each succeeding year her court will be held continuously from Christmas to Easter. The doors are open to all. Her handsome debonair Chinese cousin, under the pseudonym Indian Azalea, has been long a favorite in the floral courts of America and Europe and so, too, have other relatives, but endowed with radiant beauty this youthful, winsome Princess is bound to capture and hold the stronghold of public affection and esteem. She first came to these shores as a baby in 1916 and in 1920 a few favored folk were permitted to peep at this charming damsel in conservative Boston, Massachusetts. The effect was magical, all who saw forthwith became her devotees. Her first lover in this part of the world, her sponsor and guardian, I immediately found myself a mere atom in her universe.[24]

The Kurume collection looked like being a major introduction that by itself more than justified his sixth expedition to the Far East.[25]

In June 1918 he left Japan and returned with his family to Korea. 'We are tired of Japan,' he wrote to his mother, 'Every place there is full of Russians and things have advanced in price enormously. In Korea things are rather better and the climate is superior to that of Japan.'[26]

He spent July exploring the Diamond Mountains in the company of his wife and daughter. Muriel Wilson once described how her father carried out his photographic work on these trips. Having scouted the countryside on foot for interesting subjects, he would return at a later date with his heavy plate camera and tripod. On some of these return visits he would take his family: Nellie in a sedan chair, and Muriel on a small Russian pony. Often the party would journey for many hours only to find that conditions would not allow the object of the expedition to be carried out. The light would be too poor or the wind would set the branches of a tree in motion preventing a clear photograph from being taken. Wilson was a perfectionist, a trait that is often revealed in the quality of his pictures.

One of Wilson's personal photographs taken on one of these trips shows a rather tired-looking Nellie Wilson clad in dusty, heavy travelling clothes. At her side sits her daughter Muriel; her pose and facial expression are those of all children pressed into unpalatable activities by their parents.

Wilson spent August and September exploring the regions to the west and south of the Yalu River, and then he made a return visit to Taiwan by way of Japan. On this, his last visit to Taiwan, he decided to climb Mount Morrison (Yu Shan). At over 13,035 ft, this is the highest mountain on Taiwan, and in fact was the highest in the Japanese empire. No doubt its height, and the fact that very few Europeans had reached the summit had some part in his motives, but there were also scientific investigations to be carried out.

Nellie and Muriel sometimes accompanied Wilson on his less arduous trips into the Korean countryside.

'CHINESE' WILSON

Setting out in mid-October with a party of what Wilson describes as reformed head-hunters and their Japanese police escorts, he began the difficult ascent. 'For three days' he wrote, 'the weather was glorious and I garnered a rich harvest of botanical specimens, took many photographs of trees, and my note-book fairly bulged.'[27] Then, in sight of the summit, a typhoon struck, and Wilson and his men were forced to take shelter for three days and nights. On the morning of the seventh day of the expedition they were able to resume their climb, and finally attained their goal. The view from the summit was limited to 50 ft by the driving sleet, however, and the cheers of the conquerors were lost in the wind. 'I had brought along a pint bottle of champagne with which to celebrate our conquest,' he wrote, 'but so cold were we that I dared not risk opening the bottle until we had gained the shelter of some Junipers a thousand feet below the summit.'[28]

This success spurred him on to attempt to conquer another of Taiwan's natural obstacles. Along the north-eastern coast were towering granitic cliffs some 8000 ft high, which it seemed had never been crossed by any European. Accompanied by his usual retinue of native porters and armed Japanese, Wilson took five days to tramp through the forests at the top of the cliffs:

Everything was dank and luxuriant, and the tense silence was broken only by the dull roar of the waves of the Pacific Ocean dashing themselves against the cliffs thousands of feet below. Occasionally a bird flitted across the path or a monkey was seen in the tree-tops, but these were rare events. The armed Japanese police and the savages who carried our baggage were all silent as we trudged slowly through the wondrous primeval forests which clothe the upper parts of the world-famous sea cliffs of northeast Formosa.[29]

As the new year began Wilson prepared for his return to America. His trips on this expedition to the Far East had been much more rugged than those he had undertaken in 1914 but he was rewarded with a rich harvest of seeds and other living material. In a little under two years he had collected over 30,000 dried specimens representing over 3000 species and his camera work had yielded a collection of over 700 photographs.

Chapter Six
Touring the World for the Arnold Arboretum

The extraordinary grass trees, or 'Black boys' (*Xanthorrhoea reflexa*) of Western Australia.

Wilson returned to Boston in March 1919 and resumed his duties at the Arnold Arboretum. In April of that year, on the recommendation of Sargent, the Harvard Corporation appointed Wilson as Assistant Director of the Arboretum, a position he would hold for the next eight years.

Occupying a little office on the second floor of the Administration Building, he acted as something of a buffer for the ageing Sargent. In addition to his administrative duties he also wrote numerous articles for various gardening publications. For *Garden Magazine* he wrote a series of articles entitled 'The Romance of Our Trees', which he later enlarged upon and published as a book under the same title. He also continued with his lecturing and was a much sought-after speaker. At this time he was able to command a fee of US$ 150 as a guest speaker, a considerable sum for the 1920s.[1]

The Arnold Arboretum had amassed a wealth of living specimens as a result of the collecting expeditions it had financed over the fifty years of its existence. The great days of plant hunting, however, were soon to be drastically curtailed for United States institutions. On his return from Japan, Wilson had found that the Department of Agriculture were threatening to impound the plant material he had bought back from his sixth expedition and require the quarantine and disinfection of all imported plants. Over the years the department had become increasingly concerned about the proliferation of foreign plant pests being introduced to the United States. By 1919 a little-used law passed seven years previously regarding plant importations was being vigorously enforced, and the Secretary of Agriculture issued Quarantine Order No 37, which required that all imported plant material be disinfected at centres in Washington.

The irascible Sargent made fierce objections to what he saw as bureaucratic interference in matters scientific. He was effectively silenced, however, when officials of the Federal Horticultural Board discovered, during an inspection of the Arboretum, 'four potentially injurious species of insects [*sic*] not previously known to occur in [the U.S.A.]'.[2]

Charles Sprague Sargent was now approaching his eightieth year but his enthusiasm for the Arboretum and his desire for it to assume its 'rightful place' as a major botanical institution did not diminish. The Arnold Arboretum had been his life's work and he intended that before his death its name should be known world-wide as the foremost centre of arboreal research.

To this end he conceived an elaborate public relations exercise in which the Arboretum's greatest personality would carry its name round the world from the Americas to the Antipodes. Ernest H Wilson would undertake an eighteen-month tour of Australia, New Zealand, Tasmania, Singapore, the Federated Malay States, India and Ceylon.

94

This was not to be principally a plant collecting exercise; rather an opportunity for Wilson to meet the officials of the botanical gardens in these countries and establish lasting links between these institutions and the Arnold Arboretum for the exchange of plant materials and literature. He would also

Ernest Wilson on the steps of the administration building of the Arnold Arboretum. This photograph was taken on the very day he began his world tour.

undertake to make a good photographic record of the tour and catalogue the native trees of each country visited. The Arnold Arboretum would become a unique centre of knowledge of the woody plants of the world.

For this trip he was given the title of professor, no doubt with the intention of giving further weight to his credentials. Arrangements for his departure were speedily made, and in the summer of 1920 he had his furniture crated and put into store. First he and his family travelled to England. Nellie and Muriel would stay with his mother in Birmingham while he was away, and Wilson himself wanted to meet up with colleagues in Britain and visit the Royal Botanic Gardens, Kew, and

The giant karri trees (*Eucalyptus diversicolor*) of Western Australia.

'CHINESE' WILSON

the Royal Botanic Garden, Edinburgh, to elicit their co-operation in the Arboretum's ambitious venture.

Wilson left England on 9 September 1920 and crossed the English Channel to Boulogne. From here he travelled south by rail to Toulon where he joined his ship, the SS *Königin Luise*, due to sail for Australia on the 12th. It would arrive in Fremantle, in Western Australia, on 14 October. Conditions on board seem to have been anything but comfortable: 'This ship is an ex-German liner and very ill-found;' he wrote to Sargent:

She can only make twelve knots under the most favourable conditions and goodness knows when we shall reach Freemantle [sic]. *There are three of us in a lower deck cabin with one port hole. The ship is crowded and the bath and lavatory accommodation disgraceful. There is no laundry on board so we shall have a nice lot of linen by the time our destination is reached.*

Thus far the passage has been smooth and only comfortably warm but the Red Sea is ahead. I am longing to get to Australia and to work for I am utterly bored![3]

It is interesting that he chose to travel 'economy class' for this voyage. His position certainly warranted first-class passage, which would have been swifter as well as more comfortable. No doubt, as with previous expeditions, he was prepared to 'rough it' to keep expenses to a minimum. The cost of travel in the countries he intended visiting must have been something of an unknown quantity and a 'penny-wise' beginning to his travels would have been a sensible strategy.

Throughout this expedition Wilson kept up a regular correspondence with Sargent, sometimes business-like, sometimes chatty but always informative:

Here I am safe and sound in West Australia [sic] *and for the life of me I can't help thinking it is Southern California. The soil, the people and the abundant sunshine are all strongly suggestive of that land. There are only about 33,000 people in the whole state and Perth, the capital city, is Los Angeles in miniature. To heighten the Californian delusion the Monterey Pine and Cypress are very common trees here. The shops are ordered on American lines and much of the goods are American.*[4]

He spent a month in Western Australia in all, and covered about 1500 miles of country to the east, south and south-west of Perth. With the help of the state's chief forester, W Lane Poole, he was able to examine the most important trees in these areas, and was given herbarium specimens representing about 400 species of Australia's woody plants. He also took numerous photographs of trees.

From Jarrahdale he went out to see the country where the jarrah tree (*Eucalyptus marginata*) grew, and he went up-country from Nannup to see the famous karri forests (*Eucalyptus diversicolor*). He described the giant karri trees as 'wonderful . . . the finest broad-leaved trees I have ever seen.'[5] With regret he noted that the high-quality timber of the karri and the jarrah was used chiefly for railway sleepers – a waste of a very valuable resource, he felt.

In Western Australia, he also saw the tuart (*Eucalyptus gomphocephala*) and the 'weird and extraordinary' grass trees, or 'Black-boys' as they were known locally, noting in particular *Kingia australis* and *Xanthorrhoea preisii*. With their tufted crowns, these looked almost human in shape, and were quite unlike anything Wilson had seen anywhere else in his travels.

The local newspapers sought Wilson out wherever he travelled. Each time he was interviewed he was careful to point out the prime objectives of his mission. In the Australian *Western Mail*, for example, he explained:

I am Assistant Director of the Arnold Arboretum of Harvard University, and am working on a scheme we have to try and take a census of the world's trees and see what they are before they disappear. We have already done America, and I have spent 21 years in the Far East on the same work . . . We want to get a census of the world's trees because they are disappearing so rapidly. If we do not get such records of them in the shape of photographs and specimens, a hundred years hence many will have disappeared entirely. Our work is pure research, purely scientific; we have nothing whatsoever to do with the commercial aspect.[6]

Wilson's concern about the environment and the role of trees in preserving our global climate was reflected in various statements reported in the Australian press. 'Land improvement' schemes that involved clearing forests to plant vast fields of wheat could lead to catastrophe, he warned, pointing out that without wind-breaks, precious soil could simply be blown away. 'Arboricidal mania' was the term he used to describe the destruction of the Australian forests, and in words that sound uncannily familiar to modern ears, he explained:

Few seem to sufficiently appreciate what an important factor trees are in the wealth, health and beauty of a country. When you destroy the forests you upset the balance of nature. Besides the aspects of utility and beauty trees play an important part in health. They live on the very gas (carbon dioxide) that is poisonous to the animal kingdom, and if the vegetable kingdom were destroyed the animal kingdom would automatically die, too . . . The present generation must remember that it only holds the forests in trust for future generations.[7]

His attack on the misuse of valuable timber resources continued once he reached Adelaide, in South Australia, in November. The Americans, he stated, were the most ruthless and wasteful in their use of timber country, but the Australians came a good second: 'Timber resources are about the richest national asset that Australia possesses. Much may be thought of agricultural land and vine land, as well as the mines, but, strictly speaking, Australia's best asset is its forest land. Mines peter out, but forests are, or should be, for ever.'[8]

At the end of January 1921 Wilson began a tour of the forests of New Zealand. His passage from Australia was a smooth one, but due to a strike in Sydney he found himself on an overcrowded ship. Cabin quarters were unobtainable and he had to sleep on the floor of the dining saloon along with a dozen other men. His ship landed at Auckland, from where he planned to take a trip to see the kauri forests to the north. The kauri, *Agathis australis*, is the monarch of the New Zealand forests. In times past these trees had covered enormous tracts of land, but by the time of Wilson's visit the now familiar policy of felling and burning had taken its toll. The tree could have provided a valuable source of timber but its commercial possibilities had now been wiped out. The largest specimens seen by Wilson rose to a height of 150 ft with girths of up to 37 ft.

Wilson travelled to the south to Rotorua and then to Wellington. On his arrival there he was given a very warm welcome from the officials of the Forestry Bureau and granted immediate facilities to tour the forests of the North Island. A combination of the type of vegetation and the damp climate made it a difficult matter to prepare dried specimens and he therefore concentrated on making a photographic record of his journeys. Fortunately the forestry authorities were willing to instruct their own people to collect and prepare specimens of woody plants for Wilson, so that his herbarium collection could be complete.

Crossing to Christchurch on the South Island he travelled south to the Bluff with side trips to Queenstown on Lake Wakatipu, and to Mussel Beach, in Marlborough. Returning to Christchurch he crossed to Hokitika on the west coast and then travelled north to Nelson, where he took ship for Wellington.

In the local newspapers Wilson forcefully attacked the New Zealand government for its lethargy in the matter of devising a sensible policy for forestry. The problem, as he saw it, was the same as that which he had witnessed in Australia; the destruction of the great forests to make way for agricultural expansion. As he saw it, the current policy was shortsighted and would ultimately lead to the loss of one of New Zealand's greatest natural assets: a plentiful supply of valuable timber. He was also concerned about the use of fire to clear trees, pointing out that this would destroy essential nitrogen-fixing bacteria (present in the root nodules of leguminous plants), impoverishing the soil. The loss of the trees themselves would mean the loss of top soil, which would reduce crop yield and increase silting in harbours. 'Use, not abuse, the bush,' Wilson urged.[9]

He left New Zealand on 10 March for Sydney and there made immediate preparations for a trip to the island of Tasmania. Here he visited the botanical gardens in the capital, Hobart. These were the oldest in Australia after those in Sydney, but apparently he found them in a sorry state. Having time on his hands (he arrived in Hobart for the Easter holiday and to his great annoyance found everything shut), he decided to write an account of them. 'These criticisms are made intentionally in the hope that if published in our *Journal* they will be read by Kew and other British institutions and may possibly lead to something being done to rescue the Hobart B.G. from the deplorable condition it is now in to something like activity and usefulness,' he wrote to Sargent.[10] He clearly saw it as part of his brief to report on the well-being or otherwise of the institutions he visited.

From Hobart, he was able to travel the length and breadth of the island by rail and car. He journeyed first to Launceston in the north, and from there to what was then the small shipping port of Burnie, on the north coast. Wilson noted that the flora of north-western Tasmania was very much like that of southern Australia, with the odd-looking grass trees a striking feature.

Leaving Burnie by car he made a 70-mile journey to see a virgin blackwood swamp on the Arthur River, then travelling southwards on the Emu Bay Railway, he visited Strahan. His journey was a pleasant one through unspoilt mountainous countryside, though around settlements such as Queenstown, in the west, he could see the effects of large-scale mining activities in the form of ugly spoil heaps.

The principal trees of the island were blackwood, southern beech and numerous species of *Eucalyptus*; the blue gum (*Eucalyptus globulus*) being most conspicuous, rising to a height of 100 ft and more. The undergrowth was mainly comprised of ferns, with the impressive tree-fern, *Dicksonia antarctica*, its massive trunk often festooned with mosses and liverworts, lending a primordial appearance to the forest.

At the end of April 1921, Wilson returned to the Australian mainland and spent May and June exploring New South Wales and Queensland. The latter he found to be the richest of the Australian states in forests and it was here that he saw for the first time one of the strangest of trees. The bottle tree (*Brachychiton rupestris*) is truly an 'aristocrat of the trees'. Standing 80 ft or more in height and 30 ft in girth it looks like a gigantic bottle, its trunk tapering off at the top to form the neck. Even more strange is the fact that the tree contains a reserve of drinkable water within its

Left: Ernest Wilson among the trees of the Tasmanian forests. After visiting Tasmania, he returned to the Australian mainland to explore the forests of Queensland (right). In this photograph can be seen the striking foliage of *Archontophoenix cunninghamiana*.

trunk, which is reputed to have saved the lives of many travellers lost in the bush without water.

Wilson had been particularly dismayed by what he had seen in the forests of Queensland. Despite the fact that £¼m annually was obtained from forestry here, none of this money was reinvested by the federal government in reafforestation. As a result, the timber wealth of the state was being rapidly exhausted. Before finally quitting Australia he made one of his strongest criticisms of the Australian government. 'It is the old story – burn! burn! burn! Leave nothing for the future. But do not wonder if future generations curse your short sightedness.'[11]

On 25 June Wilson sailed from Port Darwin on the SS *Montoro*. His route to India was to be by way of Singapore and the Federated Malay States. His first stopover was in Java, where he was pleased to see the best being made of the abundant tropical resources there. Though the chief Javanese products were coffee and cocoa, he saw that extensive areas were being devoted to that increasingly important product, rubber.

What he saw in Java, however, was nothing compared with what he was to find in Malaya. Reaching Singapore in the first week of July he travelled by train to Penang, a distance of more than 300 miles. Not once, during what was a seven-hour journey, did he look from his railway carriage window and see anything other than rubber plantations. Only a few years previously this whole area would have been tropical forest.

At Kuala Lumpur, which was then the new capital city of the Federated Malay States, he was able to make further useful contacts for the Arnold Arboretum. At the forestry department here he met an American, Dr F Foxworthy, late of the Philippine Forestry Service, who was a keen botanical collector. Foxworthy was to prove of considerable help in Wilson's enterprise, readily agreeing to collect dried specimens of native flora and forward them to the United States.

He then travelled on to Calcutta, arriving on 19 July. Here he had to decide on his plans for the rest of the journey. He had originally intended to return to Boston after leaving India, but Sargent was now keen for him to extend the trip to East Africa. As it turned out, his money had gone further than expected, and he found that he could sail direct from Bombay to Mombasa.

From Calcutta he travelled all over northern India. He saw the famous deodars at Simla, and visited the garden of Nazimbagh at Srinagar, where he also saw the great plane tree planted by Shah Jahan, the Mogul emperor who built the Taj Mahal. In Assam he sought the rare Khasya pine (*Pinus kesiya*), and at Agra he admired the Taj Mahal.

Before exploring India further, he made a brief trip to Sri Lanka, to see the botanical gardens at Peradeniya. These were reputed to be most beautiful and Wilson certainly found them so: 'as well you know', he wrote to Sargent, 'the Peradeniya B.G is considered one of the finest tropical gardens in the world and this opinion is well founded.'[12]

The remainder of his trip to India was spent in the south of the country. He stayed for ten days at Ootacamund, in the Nilgiri hills, where he enjoyed fine weather and collected some 200 species. A characteristically observant letter describes the countryside around Ootacamund:

Ootacamund familiarly known as Ooty, is a hill station situated in the Nilgiri Hills at an elevation of about 7000 ft. On three sides for many miles stretch rolling grass-clad downs with scattered woods called sholas in thin folds. These sholas are often dense thickets of low, much-branched trees with relatively large trunks of great age. One of the commonest constituents of these sholas is a form of Rhod: arboreum. The woody plants are largely Chino-Himalayan types and I felt quite at home among them . . . These rolling downs were never forested but soon after Ooty became an established hill-station many kinds of Eucalyptus, Acacias and other trees from Australia were introduced and planted in quantity round the town. They flourished and today are a dominant feature of the landscape.[13]

He was to find a mixed response to his mission in this area. The curator of the botanical garden at Ootacamund had presented him with 150 specimens, but a visit to the agricultural college at Coimbatore, a little further south, was less encouraging. 'I found a couple of keen botanists from whom we shall get herb. material later on' he wrote to Sargent, 'but the forestry officials were without interest so far as our object was concerned.'[14] He blamed the lack of interest on the unsettled situation in India at the time and on what he saw as the apathy of the Indian government with regard to botanical research.

Leaving Coimbatore, he journeyed south to Bangalore and there visited the gardens of the maharaja. Wilson found that an impressive feature of Bangalore and

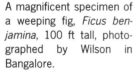

A magnificent specimen of a weeping fig, *Ficus benjamina*, 100 ft tall, photographed by Wilson in Bangalore.

'CHINESE' WILSON

the surrounding district was the large number of weeping figs (*Ficus benjamina*) growing there. As a long-established favourite of the Victorian conservatory, this plant would have been very familiar to Wilson. Today it is very popular as a house plant and Wilson himself always regarded it as 'the handsomest of all the figs'.

All in all, Wilson felt that he had had a successful tour of India. He had succeeded in obtaining a good haul of specimens and other related material and he had established many useful contacts for the future. He was, however, not a little disappointed in the quality of the work being carried out by government botanists there. Again he placed the responsibility for this with the Indian government: 'There are a number of men capable of doing great work if they only had liberty of action and were not kept ground down to a desk wasting their time and energy on pettifogging routine of little or no real value,' he wrote to Sargent.[15]

At the end of October he arrived in Bombay, where he set about making the necessary arrangements for his extended tour to central and southern Africa. Leaving Bombay on 4 November, he crossed the Indian Ocean and arrived in Mombasa nine days later. One of the things that had drawn him to Kenya was the gigantic red cedar (*Juniperus procera*), which on maturity attained a height of 150 ft and a girth of as much as 30 ft. In order to see this tree, Wilson backpacked from Nairobi with a knowledgeable forester to the land of the Kikuyu tribe. He spent two weeks out in the great forests and had a pleasant time collecting specimens and taking photographs of the giant trees there.

Another trip took him to the Aberdare Range, to the north of Nairobi. He travelled by train to Naivasha, on the shores of the great lake of the same name, and then by Overland car, scattering herds of antelope and zebra as he bumped his way over the rolling downs to the forestry station at Kinobob. The station manager, H G Deakin, accompanied him on the trek into the mountains.

From the station a broad path leads through scrub and a remnant of Red Cedar forest to a trail ascending the Aberdare Mountains. The climb is easy over a path which zigzags to the summit of the ridge some 3000 feet above the forest station. On the outskirts of the forest remnant, a tree, St John's Wort (Hypericum lanceolatum) *favorite nurse of the Red Cedar in babyhood, flaunted its rich yellow blossoms aplenty. At one point the trail passes through a broad belt of Bamboos whose stems are often 50 feet tall despite its name* Arundinaria alpina [*now called* Sinarundinaria alpina]. *As a potential source of paper-pulp this alpine Bamboo is viewed with favor, the more so because of its vast quantity. At the moment, however, its interest to me was in the fact of its being the home of wild elephants whose acquaintance I did not wish to make. The trails they make in crashing through these Bamboo-brakes were many and my companion, Forester Deakin, told that somewhere northward in the forested valley is the lordly elephant's Valhalla. It awaits discovery and the fortunate will find there rich wealth in ivory. But the giant Pachyderm is a canny, nay, uncanny beast with subtle brain stored with secrets not known to man. My forester friend had pursued many trails but only odd tusks of little value had been his reward.*[16]

  The trek was a pleasant one in cool air and brilliant sunshine. At the summit
of the range there lay an undulating basin clad in low bushes and herbs. Much of the
basin consisted of peat bog oozing brown stagnant water. Round and about were
scattered streams and tarns. Wilson and his companion crossed the basin to a rough
hut built for the use of men employed to stock some of the streams with trout.
Deakin had shot a gazelle, which provided a hot and satisfying meal for them. 'As
the sun dipped below the horizon the temperature rapidly declined also,' Wilson
wrote:

We lodged about half a degree south of the Equator but at just over 11,000 feet altitude and we were glad to hug a large fire in an open grate. Delightfully tired after a wonderful day we retired early and crowded on the blankets. About 3 A.M. my Good Fairy awakened me and told me to look outside. Obeying the voice I opened the door and stepped without. Amazement was mine. The moon was dipping on the horizon, the Milky Way hung a perfect arc immediately over my head, its glistening myriad stars shone with startling brilliancy, the darting facets of light of an intenseness that could be felt. So near they seemed that I could almost clutch them with upraised hands; the ground around was white with hoar frost which threw back the sparkling rays rippling with laughter. The earth, myself and all around me were enveloped in the ethereal glory of the star-set heavens. Not before nor since have I witnessed so sublime a spectacle as on the summit of the Aberdare range. And I murmured a prayer of thanks to the Good Fairy as shivering but elated I went inside the hut and crawled beneath my blankets.[17]

In December 1921 Wilson was in Kisumu, on the north-eastern shore of Lake Victoria. Boarding 'a neat up-to-date steamer' here, he made the twenty-four-hour voyage across the lake to Entebbe in Uganda: 'That great African traveller, Stanley, in 1875 christened Uganda the "Pearl of Africa",' he wrote, 'and I found it so too. Richly forested, well watered, capable of producing vast riches from cotton, coffee, cocoa and other tropical crops it has a great future.'[18]

Generally he found the forests of Uganda less interesting than those of Kenya, though he thought two species of tree worthy of special note: the upas (*Antiaris toxicaria*) and the aptly named sausage tree (*Kigelia aethiopica*, now called *K. africana*), which he described as 'a strange looking fellow, low of stature, with wide-spreading crown strung in season with bologna sausage-like fruits.'[19] The former was alleged to emit deadly vapours that would kill anyone incautious enough to sleep beneath it. This, Wilson commented, 'is merely a legend and a gross libel on a stately tree. The tree is perfectly innocuous but frequently grows in deep valleys where hangs heavy carbonic-acid [carbon dioxide] gas deadly to man and animals alike – hence the origin of this myth.'[20]

Towards the end of 1921, he was able to realise a boyhood ambition. In *Plant Hunting* he recalls how, in his youth, he had dreamt of the exploits of the great African explorer Speke, who had discovered Lake Victoria, which he believed to be the source of the Nile. Wilson's visit to the port of Jinja, where the Victoria Nile arises, was therefore an act of homage twice over:

I sat on the edge of the Ripon falls and watched the waters of the Victoria Nyanza tumble over the cliff and give birth to the River Nile. The holy Nile like the gods of old is born adult. No bubbling of some petty spring gives it birth, none but the waters of Africa's largest lake suffice. A vent in the rim of the lake three quarters of a mile wide over which rushed some 500 cubic metres of water per second is the birthplace of this mighty river . . . As fittingly becomes a pilgrim I descended to the river's edge, lay down and drank deep of the sweet waters.[21]

Returning to Mombasa, he then travelled south to Beira and via what was then Salisbury to Bulawayo. Here he managed to do some collecting and visited the tomb of Cecil Rhodes, high in the Matopo hills. In general the itinerary Sargent demanded did not make it possible for Wilson to devote much time to systematic collecting himself. Instead he made arrangements with individuals willing to make a contribution to the expedition.

From Bulawayo he travelled north-west to Livingstone, near the Victoria Falls:

'There they are, there they are!' excitedly shouted my fellow travellers on the train I had boarded sixteen hours before at Bulawayo as it toiled across the savannahs towards the Victoria Falls. Following their gaze I saw white plume-like clouds floating in the sky and knew that they were immense volumes of spray shot up from the famed Falls of the Zambesi River. The train was twelve to fifteen miles distant from the Falls but on calm days these clouds of spray in five columns are visible at propitious seasons from a distance of twenty-five miles. The natives call them 'Mosi-oa-tunya', the smoke that thunders – a pleasing and appropriate name.[22]

Below the falls, shrouded permanently in mist and spray, Wilson found *Gladiolus primulinus* (now called *G. natalensis*), growing in its natural habitat. The plant has a curious adaption to its unusual environment. Its erect pale yellow flower spikes are each sheltered by a hooded upper petal, which keeps the pollen-bearing stamens dry. This plant had been collected by Francis Fox, who had built the famous cantilever railway bridge nearby, and introduced by him to England.

'The smoke that thunders'. A photograph taken by Wilson of the 'Devil's cauldron', part of the Victoria Falls.

'CHINESE' WILSON

The baobab or cream of tartar tree was another plant peculiar to Africa that Wilson found growing near the falls:

the baobab is one of the giants of the vegetable world, but because of the fact it was so large [early travellers] got exaggerated ideas of its age, and jumped at conclusions in this respect. They said that here was a tree that started in the Garden of Eden, that was as old as the

Top: A good example of a baobab tree, *Adansonia digitata*, photographed by Wilson in Mombasa.

Bottom: When in South Africa, Wilson made time to see the famous Clanwilliam cedars, *Widdringtonia juniperoides*, photographed here on Table Mountain.

world. Well, when you see a tree for the first time that is 60, 70 or 80 feet in girth, you are apt to think that it is very, very ancient ... The baobab [however] is one of the fastest-growing trees in the world ... but it is not a long-lived tree ... It has no hardwood as we understand the term. It is all pith and pulp. A bullet from a rifle would go right through one.[23]

The common name for the tree is derived from the white powdery substance, tasting like cream of tartar, found inside its egg-shaped fruit. David Livingstone carved his initials on one of these trees when he discovered the falls in 1851. Wilson was able to visit this same tree and found that the great explorer's carvings were still clearly discernible.

His next destination was Pretoria, at the heart of the Transvaal. He was given a warm welcome here and the chief conservator of forests arranged for him to see the forests of Natal, Zululand and Knysna, and the famous cedars at Clanwilliam, to the north of Cape Town. He also had the opportunity to visit Cape Town itself, and to explore the lower slopes of Table Mountain, where he saw the only true *Amaryllis*, the belladonna lily, growing wild.

He enjoyed his time in South Africa – he found the people friendly and helpful and he was able to collect at leisure – but he was now more than ready to go home. In April 1922 he sailed from Cape Town to Southampton and, rejoining his family, arrived back in Boston in August. He had been away from America for more than two years.

A portrait of Ernest Wilson taken after his plant hunting days were over, used as a publicity photograph for his books.

Chapter Seven
The Final Years in Boston

In 1922 Sargent had attained the age of eighty-one and he was in his fiftieth year as Director of the Arnold Arboretum. During this first half-century Sargent had built up the reputation of this institution to one of world-wide renown, a reputation which was owed in no small part to the globe-trotting activities of its Assistant Director, Ernest Wilson. Its financial position, however, was less secure, mainly as a result of an extensive – and expensive – building programme. It was against this background that Wilson resumed his duties.

The slim prospects of any financial advancement no doubt acted as something of a fillip to his writing activities. Initially he continued to write for professional journals, continuing his association with the British horticultural periodical, *Gardeners' Chronicle*. In America he wrote regularly for the *Journal of the Arnold Arboretum*, and published numerous articles for *Horticulture*, the journal of the Massachusetts Horticultural Society, for which he was later to become a trustee and advisory editor. Wilson also found time to publish in less scholarly works such as *Garden Magazine* and *House and Garden*. These publications were primarily intended for the amateur gardener and plant enthusiast. It was one of Wilson's strengths as a writer that he could vary his style to suit his readership. His popular articles are entertaining as well as informative.

In 1925 he began his association with the Stratford Company of Boston, who were to publish all his remaining books, including *If I Were to Make a Garden*, which was published posthumously, assembled from a manuscript Wilson had been working on at the time of his death. His first book to be published by Stratford was *America's Greatest Garden*, in which he describes the history and achievements of the Arnold Arboretum. This book is intended for a general readership and it is here that Wilson reveals his admiration for the institution's initiator, Charles Sargent, and his delight in a botanical garden which he rates second in his affection only to the Royal Botanic Gardens at Kew. Wilson did not intend this to be a guidebook but rather an invitation to the reader to sample what was on offer at the Arboretum throughout the four seasons.

The text of this book, as was usually the case with Wilson's popular works, is generously illustrated with photographs taken with the author's own camera. Wilson's family would often accompany him on photographic expeditions around New England and could find themselves posing in front of the camera lens. Sometimes, no doubt, Wilson would require this out of sentiment but more often, one suspects, this was a means of lending scale to the particular plant he was photographing. In one picture of native grape-vines, for example, illustrating *America's Greatest Garden*, the reader will see the five-year-old daughter of the plant hunter, Muriel Wilson, dressed in summer frock and flower-decorated straw hat.

It is the quality as well as quantity of the photographic illustrations in Wilson's books that sets them apart from the works of other authors of the period writing in the same field. It must have been a source of annoyance to Wilson that the technology for producing colour photographs had not been developed. The disparity between what he had originally seen projected on to the ground-glass plate at the focal plane of his camera lens and the final processed monochrome image must surely have been a disappointment to him.

The following year a new edition of *Aristocrats of the Garden* appeared. This popular work, originally published in 1917, was intended for the keen amateur gardener, and is packed with useful advice on plant selection and cultivation. Wilson had firm views about gardening procedures and the prologue of the book sets out a number of maxims and homilies on such important activities as planting and pruning. His advice is based upon a lifetime's experience dating back to his early years as a youthful gardening apprentice and carries the weight of the real expert. Some of his advice, however, might cause a nervous shiver in some of today's gardening experts:

Always have the holes for trees and shrubs well prepared and make them much wider than the ball of the plant that is to be placed therein. Dynamite is cheaper than digging and in every way much better. Half to a whole stick of Atlas Farm Powder forty per cent inserted from 2 to 3 feet down and exploded will loosen ordinary land from 6 to 10 feet downwards and outward.[1]

Lilies of Eastern Asia was published in 1925 by Dulau of London. A scientific work of great merit, consisting of a series of monographs on the genus *Lilium*, it remains today an important reference work, though some of Wilson's descriptions and nomenclature would now require revision. Even so, the work is still in print and is considered an important acquisition for the bookshelf of any serious lily cultivator.

The book that Wilson would perhaps himself choose as the one by which he would wish to be remembered was issued in 1927. *Plant Hunting* is a magnificent two-volume work containing the summation of a lifetime's work in this field. As well as giving a historical account of plant hunting through the ages, including the great plant collectors such as Francis Masson, Carl Thunberg and Joseph Banks, Wilson describes his own travels, modestly and simply, taking the reader around the world to the places he visited as a plant hunting expert: Japan, Taiwan, Australia, New Zealand, Tasmania, Kenya and South Africa. *Plant Hunting* reads as well today as when it was first published, and its reappearance in paperback in 1985 is testimony to its enduring qualities.

The year 1927 was the year in which the Arnold Arboretum lost its greatest champion. Charles Sprague Sargent died on the evening of 22 March, just a month before his 86th birthday. The end had been swift, coming after a brief attack of intestinal influenza. As Assistant Director, Wilson took over the administrative duties of the Arboretum. One of his most immediate tasks was to try to make some

THE FINAL YEARS IN BOSTON

sense of the institution's finances. At this time another costly expedition to the Chinese interior was in progress, led by the renowned collector Joseph Rock. One of Wilson's first duties in his new role was to recall Rock, in order to save money.[2]

Sargent's death was certainly a blow to the Arboretum. He had exercised great skill in the handling of the institution's finances, whereas Wilson had little experience in this area. Indeed he soon began to fear that he might be faced with a financial disaster. That the President and Fellows of Harvard had their reservations about Wilson's ability to fill the vacuum left by Sargent's death is shown by the administrative reorganisation that took place in 1927. The post of Director ceased, and overall control of the Arboretum passed to a council responsible for all the university's botanical collections, including its botanical museum and its tropical garden at Soledad in Cuba. Wilson became Keeper of the Arboretum, with the chairman of the council, Professor Oakes Ames, acting as his supervisor.

In spite of his new administrative responsibilities, Wilson still found time to continue with his writing. *More Aristocrats of the Garden* was published in 1928 as a companion volume to the 1926 work. A year later his publishers issued what is probably the most beautiful of all his books. *China, Mother of Gardens* is a delightful volume in all respects. Tastefully bound in black and gold buckram and well illustrated with plates from Wilson's own photographs, it is mainly a reissue of his first book, *A Naturalist in Western China*. Wilson had chosen his publishers well. The quality of all the books Stratford published for him is very high. Today, his books are eagerly sought by collectors, the most prized being the two volumes of *Plant Hunting* and the single-volume work, *China, Mother of Gardens*.

His last book was published in 1930, the year of his death. *Aristocrats of the Trees* is a larger-format work, once again lavishly illustrated, mainly with photographs by the author. This is no dry treatise on arboreal excellence, nor does it concentrate on exotics at the expense of the more common trees. His aim was to show that all trees – the oak, the elm and the beech as well as the cedar of Lebanon and the ginkgo – are of interest and value, and his enthusiasm for trees, and his belief in their vital importance for mankind, are reflected throughout:

In the Bible we are told that in the first garden God planted 'The Tree of Knowledge of Good and Evil', and in the old Norse Sagas the Oak and Ash are frequently mentioned. Priest and poet in every land have sung their praises and down the ages a mighty literature on tree lore has been accumulated. From early times trees have afforded man shelter, food, and clothing, and have exercised a tremendous influence over his daily life. The more simple the people the greater their appreciation, at least so it would seem since as nations became civilized they one and all by fire and axe have destroyed the friendly trees and of these vandals the white man ranks head and shoulders above all others. From the early stages of his colonizing days down to within a few years of the present, wherever he has gone he has laid waste the tree wealth of the lands in an effort, often in vain, to make a blade of corn grow where two trees grew before.[3]

His words are as true today as they were when the book was first published, and it is not surprising that this is yet another of his books to have been reprinted in recent years.

The Wilsons were now living in the Jamaica Plain area of Boston, at 380 South Street. The house was a large one, set well back from the tree-lined street, and very close to the south side of the Arboretum. Muriel had married in 1929, and had moved to Geneva in New York State, but the Wilsons were not living alone. They shared their home with Betty Mumford, a family companion who Wilson regarded almost as an adopted daughter and to whom he dedicated *More Aristocrats of the Garden*.[4]

Although Muriel was now living at some distance from Boston, the family remained close. George Slate, Muriel's husband, was a pomologist working for the New York State Agricultural Experiment Station. At this point he was researching soft fruits, but he later became an expert on lilies, and wrote the authoritative book *Lilies for American Gardens*. Clearly he had much in common with Wilson.

Wilson often joked that he despised walking once he had learnt to drive. His first car was a six-cylinder Jewett, pictured here. Mrs Wilson is seated at the front and Betty Mumford is standing outside the car.

Opposite: Ernest Henry Wilson in his South Street garden after receiving his honorary doctorate from Trinity College, Hartford. In the background can be seen his regal lilies.

In June 1930, Trinity College, Hartford, Connecticut awarded Wilson an honorary doctorate in science. He was delighted to receive such recognition for his life's work, and took great pride in the award. However, he had always found his deepest satisfaction in the work itself, and the opportunities it gave him to explore and enjoy the natural world:

Sometimes friends have said 'You must have endured much hardship wandering in out of the way corners of the earth.' I have. But such count for nothing, since I have lived in Nature's boundless halls and drank deeply of her pleasures. To wander through a tropical or temperate forest with tree-trunks more stately than gothic columns, beneath a canopy of foliage more lovely in its varied forms than the roof of any building fashioned by man, the welcome cool, the music of the babbling brook, the smell of mother earth and the mixed odors of a myriad of flowers – where does hardship figure when the reward is such?[5]

Tragically there was to be little more time to enjoy such rewards. On 15 October, while travelling back to Boston from a trip to Geneva, the Wilsons' car spun off the road and plunged 40 ft down a steep embankment. Nellie was already dead when she was pulled from the wreckage; Wilson died of his injuries within an hour of the accident. The only survivor of the tragedy was their little dog, a Boston terrier, who escaped with cuts and bruises.

Everyone who had known them was stunned by the news. 'Chinese' Wilson had seemed indestructible. His exploits in western China – braving landslides,

The Wilson-Slates. George Slate and Muriel Wilson were married in April 1929 and moved to Geneva, New York State.

armed rebellion and snowstorms – were legendary and it seemed deeply ironic that such a man should meet his death on a suburban highway less than 60 miles from home.

A double funeral service was held in Boston on the Saturday following the accident. It was attended by leading figures in horticulture from all over North America, and the caskets were covered in floral tributes representing Wilson's plant introductions. There was a spray of his favourite flowering crab, *Malus toringoides*, introduced by him from the Sino-Tibetan border in 1904, branches of the tea crabapple, *Malus theifera* (now called *Malus hupehensis*), and the tree honeysuckle, *Lonicera maackii*. From the ravines of western China, there was the rock spray, *Cotoneaster microphyllus*, and representing his travels in Japan, a spray of the blue beauty berry, *Callicarpa japonica*. On the very top, his colleagues had placed a green branch of the handkerchief tree.

The service was followed by cremation at the Forest Hills cemetery. It was originally planned to erect a memorial to Wilson here, within sight of the Arboretum, but in fact the final resting place for the Wilsons' remains was in Canada, at the Mount Royal Cemetery, Montreal.[6] This is where his monument stands, at the entrance to Lilac Knoll, an area that he himself helped to design, with a fittingly simple inscription: 'ERNEST HENRY WILSON . . . "whose ardour as an explorer and judgment as a collector added to our gardens many eastern Asiatic plants"'.[7]

The striking white bracts of the handkerchief tree, *Davidia involucrata*, possibly Wilson's most famous introduction.

Chapter Eight
Wilson's Living Legacy
VICTORIA MATTHEWS

E H Wilson has supreme importance as a plant collector: he introduced over 1000 species into western gardens, and certainly more trees and shrubs than any other collector. Many of his introductions proved to be new to science, indeed he found a number of new genera, including one in the Hamamelidaceae which the botanist Hemsley named *Sinowilsonia*, this being the Latin translation of 'Chinese' Wilson.

Wilson tended to concentrate more on trees and shrubs than on herbaceous plants and certainly the documentation of the woody plants is more extensive. However, it was not only his plant introductions that were of great value, but also his collections of dried plants. In effect he served two masters: the botanical institution whose interest lay in herbarium material, and the gardener keen to grow new plants.[1] Wilson collected over 18,000 herbarium specimens, most of which are kept in the Herbarium of the Arnold Arboretum, although there are duplicate specimens in many other herbaria around the world. Nor should his contribution as a photographer be underestimated: he made over 5000 glass plate photographs for the Arnold Arboretum, as well as another 5000 nitrate-base negatives, of both plants and places. The importance of the latter is that Wilson photographed places which have now changed completely, or no longer exist – thus providing a historical record of areas which he visited.

The trees and shrubs which Wilson found in China are catalogued in *Plantae Wilsonianae*, published in three volumes between 1911 and 1917 and edited by C S Sargent, with contributions from Wilson himself and Alfred Rehder, his colleague at the Arnold Arboretum (see chapter 5).[2] As always, Wilson's descriptions are both vivid and accurate and I have quoted directly from them wherever possible. There is no room here to list or describe all the plants which Wilson sent back to the West, so I have selected some of the more important or more beautiful ones, which I hope will give a taste of the rich treasure trove which Wilson uncovered. We should be immensely grateful to this enthusiastic and successful plant collector, who contributed so much to our gardens.

Abelia schumannii (Caprifoliaceae)
A small deciduous shrub (colour pl. 9) which produces masses of lilac-pink, slightly scented flowers in late summer and autumn. The flowers have orange blotches. The calyx persists after the corolla has fallen. It needs to be grown in a sunny, sheltered position, as it is not completely hardy in northern Europe and will be cut back severely in a cold winter. However, unless the plants are very young, they will grow up again the following spring.

Abies (Pinaceae)

Silver firs

There are some fifty silver firs, evergreen conifers coming mainly from the northern hemisphere. They grow best in a moist climate. _Abies fargesii_ was first found by the missionary Père Farges, after whom it was named, and introduced by Wilson in 1901. It is more commonly cultivated in the United States than in Britain, where it is very rare – a pity as it is a beautiful tree with purplish cones up to 10 cm long. _Abies recurvata_, often known as the Min fir, was introduced in 1910 from the valley of the Min River in Sichuan. Its name refers to the leaves which, on the upper sides of the branchlets, are strongly recurved. The young cones are violet. Also rarely grown is _A. squamata_, which has peeling, shaggy, brown-purple bark, and which also came from Sichuan in 1910.

Acer (Aceraceae)

Maples

There are over 100 species of maple, native to the temperate regions of the northern hemisphere. One of the most attractive is the paperbark maple, _A. griseum_ (colour pl. 18), which Wilson introduced from central China in 1901. The common name refers to the bark, which on older trees curls back in patches to reveal the cinnamon-brown to orange-brown underlayer. The three-lobed leaves turn scarlet in the autumn.

Wilson introduced many other maples, including _A. cappadocicum_ var. _sinicum_, _A. davidii_ (colour pl. 4), _A. erianthum_, _A. flabellatum_, _A. franchetii_, _A. henryi_, _A. maximowiczii_, _A. multiserratum_, _A. oblongum_ var. _concolor_, _A. oliverianum_, _A. tetramerum_ and _A. wilsonii_.

Aconitum (Ranunculaceae)

Monkshoods

The monkshoods are useful garden perennials with purple, blue or yellow flowers. There are over 300 species, native to the temperate zone of the northern hemisphere, and all species are poisonous. _Aconitum hemsleyanum_, a beautiful climbing species with deep purple-blue flowers, was introduced from China. _Aconitum wilsonii_ (now called _A. carmichaelii_ var. _wilsonii_) also came from China and is a lovely plant which can grow to 2 metres in height and bears panicles of deep purple flowers.

Actinidia deliciosa (Actinidiaceae)

Kiwi fruit, Chinese gooseberry

Wilson introduced this plant (colour pl. 10) under the name _A. chinensis_, and it was known by this name until recently. A vigorous climber, the twining stems reach 9 metres if allowed, and bear large, heart-shaped leaves and clusters of cream, fragrant flowers which appear in late summer. The fruits are egg-shaped, 4–5 cm long, and covered in rough brown hairs; the flesh is green, juicy and edible, and

1 *Meconopsis integrifolia*

This page:

2 (above)
Lilium regale

3 (right)
Rhododendron fargesii

Facing page, clockwise from top left:

4 This specimen of *Acer davidii* in the memorial garden at Chipping Campden was grown by Roy Lancaster from seed collected from one of Wilson's original locations in China; it was planted by Wilson's granddaughter, Mrs Barbara Abbott.

5 *Cornus kousa* var. *chinensis*

6 *Viburnum betulifolium*

7 *Sorbus hupehensis*

PLATES

'CHINESE' WILSON

Facing page, clockwise from top:

8 *Kolkwitzia amabilis*
9 *Abelia schumannii*
10 *Actinidia deliciosa*

This page:

11 *Magnolia wilsonii*

This page:

12 (right)
Rosa moyesii
13 (below)
Davidia involucrata

Facing page, clockwise from top left:

14 *Clematis montana* var. *rubens*
15 *Parthenocissus henryana*
16 *Rheum alexandrae*
17 *Primula pulverulenta*

'CHINESE' WILSON

PLATES

Below:

18 (top)
Acer griseum

19 (bottom)
Magnolia sprengeri 'Diva'

Right:

20 (top)
Rhododendron orbiculare

21 (bottom)
Cypripedium tibeticum

contains high levels of vitamin C. The fruit is usually eaten fresh, but can be tinned or frozen (with a resultant loss of flavour).

The plants are either male or female, so to obtain fruit at least one plant of each sex must be planted: on a commercial scale, only one male is necessary for the pollination of every eight females. Kiwi fruit are now grown as a crop in New Zealand, Australia, South Africa, the United States and Chile as well as in parts of Europe, including the Channel Islands. Growing plants are susceptible to frost damage.

Albizia julibrissin (Leguminosae)

A graceful deciduous tree reaching 10 metres or more, which is commonly planted in regions with a subtropical or Mediterranean climate, but needs the protection of a wall in northern latitudes. The leaves are feathery and the flowers are pink 'powder-puffs', carried in clusters at the ends of the branches. Native over a wide area from Iran to China, it was first introduced into Europe in 1745. In 1918 Wilson introduced a hardier form with particularly fine bright pink flowers – it was one of the last plants which he sent to the Arnold Arboretum. This form is known as 'Ernest Wilson' in the United States and more prosaically as 'Rosea' in Europe.

Astilbe (Saxifragaceae)

Astilbes are superficially similar to *Aruncus* and some spiraeas (which belong to the Rosaceae) and are extremely useful garden plants, being very hardy, happy in sun or partial shade, and able to grow in badly drained conditions. They all come from the Far East and Wilson was responsible for the introduction of three species. *Astilbe grandis* is a handsome plant, growing up to 1.5 metres tall and bearing large panicles of white flowers – it is useful for the back of a herbaceous border. *Astilbe koreana* is smaller, reaching about 50 cm, and has creamy white flowers which open from pink buds: as its name implies, Wilson found it in Korea. *Astilbe chinensis* var. *davidii* (introduced as *A. davidii*) has rose-purple flowers in narrow heads and can grow to 2 metres.

Berberis (Berberidaceae)

Wilson introduced some twenty species of this genus of useful and ornamental shrubs. They are grown both for their yellow flowers (solitary or in clusters) and their fruits, which may be blue (*B. kawakamii*, introduced about 1918); black (*B. sargentiana*, introduced in 1907); pink (*B. dictyoneura*, introduced in 1910) or red (*B. francisci-ferdinandii*, introduced in 1900). *Berberis wilsoniae* (named after Wilson's wife) is perhaps one of his most attractive introductions with its pale yellow flowers and abundant bunches of translucent coral-red berries.

Betula albosinensis (Betulaceae)

This birch can grow to 30 metres in height and is cultivated (although not commonly, which is a little surprising) for its beautiful bark. Wilson wrote 'Usually it grows mixed with other deciduous leaved trees, but occasionally it forms almost pure woods . . . The bark is bright orange to orange-red, peeling off in very thin sheets, each successive sheet being covered with white glaucous bloom.'[3]

Camellia cuspidata (Theaceae)

Not one of the most spectacular camellias, but one which has proved useful in hybridisation. It grows about 2 metres or more tall and the young foliage is a pretty coppery colour. The white flowers are about 4 cm in diameter with six or seven petals. Crossed with *C. japonica* it has produced 'Candle Glow', which has white flowers with pink centres, and crossed with *C. saluenensis*, the famous 'Cornish Snow', with prolific small white flowers; 'Michael', which is similar but, with larger flowers; and 'Winton', in which the flowers are pale pink. Wilson introduced *C. cuspidata* in 1900 from western China.

Ceratostigma willmottianum (Plumbaginaceae)

In 1908 Wilson found this beautiful shrub in the Min River valley in Sichuan, the same valley where he discovered *Lilium regale*. Seed was sent to the enthusiastic gardener Miss Ellen Willmott of Warley Place in Essex, and she raised two plants – from which all the plants now grown in British gardens are derived. *Ceratostigma willmottianum* grows about 1 metre tall and produces heads of eye-catching bright blue flowers from July until the first frosts of autumn. The leaves are deciduous and turn red before they fall. It is not fussy about soil, but does best in full sun.

Cercis racemosa (Leguminosae)

Cercis is a small genus of trees: there are seven species, coming from North America, China and the Mediterranean area. The best known are *C. siliquastrum*, the Judas tree, and *C. canadensis*, the redbud of North America. *Cercis racemosa* differs from the other species in carrying its rose-pink pea-flowers in drooping twenty-five to forty-flowered racemes rather than in clusters of four to ten. Wilson introduced it in 1907 from the province of Hubei.

Cladrastis sinensis (Leguminosae)

Wilson found this small to medium-sized tree in Hubei and introduced it in 1901. It is particularly useful because it produces its large clusters of flowers, white tinged with pink, in July, when the majority of trees have finished flowering. It is also late coming into leaf: generally it is early summer before the pinnate leaves appear. *Cladrastis sinensis* deserves to be grown more widely. Wilson also introduced *C. wilsonii*, but it has no particular horticultural value and is only occasionally cultivated.

Clematis (Ranunculaceae)

Clematis are very popular garden plants. There are about 200 wild species, although not all have garden value, and hundreds of large-flowered cultivars which have been produced by plant breeders. Wilson introduced thirteen different clematis, of which the most commonly grown are *C. armandii* and *C. montana* var. *rubens* (colour pl. 14). *Clematis armandii* is a vigorous evergreen climber which can grow to 10 metres tall. In the spring it produces creamy white flowers, 5–6.5 cm across, which are strongly vanilla-scented. The glossy green leaves have three leathery, three-veined leaflets. It was named after Père Armand David, the French missionary who first found it in China. In Britain it is best grown on a south-facing wall as it can be damaged by hard frost.

There are two cultivars which are commercially available: 'Apple Blossom' has white flowers flushed with pink and leaves which are bronze when young; 'Snowdrift' has pure white flowers. Unfortunately, the plants sold by nurseries are not always correctly named, so it is best to buy flowering plants so that you can see what you are getting.

Clematis montana var. *rubens* covers itself with pink flowers every spring and sometimes has a second, although less prolific, flowering later in the year. 'The foliage of this variety is very dark coloured and readily distinguishes the plant when out of flower', Rehder and Wilson commented,[4] and certainly the dark leaves, tinged with reddish purple are most attractive.

Wilson also introduced *C. tangutica* var. *obtusiuscula* with its ferny leaves and dangling yellow lanterns, *C. potaninii* var. *souliei* with white flowers 5 cm across, produced from June to September, and *C. grata*, somewhat similar to our own traveller's joy but with white rather than cream flowers.

Cornus kousa var. *chinensis* (Cornaceae)

Cornus kousa is a large shrub or small tree which produces insignificant flowerheads, each surrounded by four conspicuous white bracts. Var. *chinensis* (colour pl. 5) is a taller, more spreading shrub with larger leaves which lacks the tufts of hairs beneath found in var. *kousa*. This cornus is hardy and will grow in any soil provided it is fairly rich and well-drained. It flowers in June; the bracts are greenish as they expand, but turn white and last for several weeks. The flowers are produced so abundantly in a good year that they almost hide the branches, and are followed by fruits which resemble long-stalked, dangling, pinkish strawberries. In the autumn the leaves turn crimson before they fall.

Corydalis wilsonii (Papaveraceae)

One of the most attractive species of *Corydalis*, with grey-green or blue-green leaves and spikes of deep yellow flowers. Much prized as a rock-garden plant, it flowers from May to July. Its only disadvantage is that it dislikes too much moisture in winter and so has to be given some sort of protection such as having a pane of glass placed over it, or grown in an alpine house.

Cotoneaster (Rosaceae)

A horticulturally important genus of fifty species distributed in north temperate regions of the Old World: Wilson introduced over twenty species, of which the most well known are *C. dammeri*, *C. divaricatus*, *C. floccosus*, *C. glabratus*, *C. perpusillus* and *C. zabelii*. These shrubs can be evergreen or deciduous and vary from prostrate plants such as *C. dammeri*, which is often used as a ground-cover on banks, to *C. floccosus*, which can reach 5 metres. They are grown both for their clusters of white flowers and their autumn display of berries, which may be black (*C. foveolatus* – introduced by Wilson in 1908) to scarlet (*C. dielsianus* – introduced 1900) or dark purplish red (*C. ambiguus* – introduced 1903).

Cypripedium (Orchidaceae)

Lady's-slipper orchids

Orchids always provoke a reaction – either pro or con! The cypripediums are orchids of the north temperate zone and their common name refers to the large, pouched lip of the flower, which is fancifully said to resemble a slipper.

Cypripedium flavum was introduced under the name *luteum* – it has beautiful soft yellow flowers – and grows up to 30 cm tall. *Cypripedium tibeticum* (colour pl. 21) is dwarfer and has rather hairy leaves and fat pinkish-purple flowers with pale-veined sepals and petals and a darker-coloured pouch. These species grow best in slightly shady, dampish conditions, or may be grown in pots in a glasshouse or cold-frame.

Neither of these species is commonly cultivated. Plants are occasionally offered for sale and one should take care that they have not been collected from the wild – only plants raised in cultivation should be purchased. Many orchids are now threatened in their native habitats and unscrupulous dealers may illegally offer wild plants.

Davidia involucrata (Davidiaceae)

Dove or handkerchief tree

This is possibly Wilson's most famous introduction (colour pl. 13), which was first discovered in 1869 by the French missionary, Père David, and named after him by a French botanist called Baillon. The story of its introduction has been told in chapter 1 of this book. It is generally considered that there are two varieties of *D. involucrata* – trees with hairy leaves belong to the type variety, var. *involucrata*, whereas trees with hairless leaves are called var. *vilmoriniana*. The latter variety is more commonly grown in gardens and is somewhat more hardy: in China it has a more easterly distribution. Botanists are undecided as to the correct status of these varieties. Differences in fruit shape have suggested that var. *vilmoriniana* should be a species in its own right, but more studies on wild populations are needed before a decision can be made.

Whether it is one species or two, it cannot be denied that the handkerchief tree is both spectacular and unusual. The leaves are similar to those of a lime tree and the flowers are produced in May, when the tree becomes covered in white 'handkerchiefs'. These are in fact huge bracts – each spherical flowerhead has two, or occasionally three (the actual flowers are rather inconspicuous). The bracts are unequal in size and the largest can measure as much as 20 cm long and 10 cm wide, although usually somewhat less. A tree in full flower is a breathtaking sight and never fails to attract attention. The handkerchief tree is deciduous, and once the leaves have fallen in autumn, the egg-shaped fruits (about 3 cm long) are revealed, hanging from the twigs on long stalks.

Iris wilsonii (Iridaceae)

This species is related to the Siberian iris, *Iris sibirica*, a popular garden plant. Within this group of irises, only two species have yellow flowers, and *I. wilsonii* is one of them, the other being *I. forrestii*, which was introduced by, and named after, the plant collector George Forrest. *Iris wilsonii* grows up to 75 cm tall and each stem carries two scented flowers 6–8 cm across. It is a promiscuous species and readily hybridises with other related irises, often producing some strangely coloured progeny. Like other Siberian irises it likes a rich soil which does not dry out, and will thrive in sun or semi-shade. The leaves die down in the winter.

Jasminum mesnyi (Oleaceae)

Primrose jasmine

A beautiful, evergreen, climbing jasmine, which was originally called *J. primulinum*. It is a close relation of *J. nudiflorum*, the winter jasmine, but has larger, soft yellow flowers which are semi-double and produced from March to May. Slightly tender, it is best grown against a sheltered south-facing wall or given the protection of a conservatory.

Kolkwitzia amabilis (Caprifoliaceae)

Beauty bush

The genus was named after Richard Kolkwitz, who was a professor of botany in Germany at the beginning of this century. *Kolkwitzia amabilis* (colour pl. 8) is a deciduous shrub up to 3.5 metres tall, which produces, in May and June, abundant clusters of pink bell-shaped flowers, each with a yellow throat and nestling in a bristly calyx. The fruit is also covered in reddish bristles and is topped by a long 'beak' carrying the calyx, which persists after the flowers have fallen. Thus the plant is also attractive in fruit.

This is a very hardy plant which likes a sunny position and a chalky soil, although it will tolerate acid soils also. Propagation from cuttings is easy. It is more commonly grown in the United States than in Britain. A cultivar named 'Pink Cloud', which has larger flowers, was raised at the Royal Horticultural Society's garden at Wisley in 1946.

Ligularia dentata (Compositae)

A spectacular perennial with stout stems up to 1.3 metres topped by deep yellow daisies, which Wilson introduced in 1900 under the name *Senecio clivorum*. The large leaf-blades are roundish, often purplish beneath, and carried on long stalks.

This species demands a rich, moist soil to grow well, and a sunny position, and looks especially fine reflected in water when it is grown by a pond or stream. Snails and slugs relish the young leaves, so it is wise to protect it from their advances if at all possible.

Lilium regale (Liliaceae)

A beautiful lily (colour pl. 2) whose stems carry up to twenty-five funnel-shaped flowers. The strongly fragrant flowers are white with a yellow throat, and are flushed with pinkish purple on the outside. It is a vigorous, easily grown lily which will flourish in sun or semi-shade, and in any soil provided the drainage is good. Wilson introduced it first in 1903 (under another name), and later in 1910 after undergoing problems and hardship (see chapter 4). A magnificent plant which is considered by many to be one of his finest introductions.

Other lilies introduced by Wilson are *L. davidii* var. *willmottiae*, *L. duchartrei* and *L. sargentiae* (named after Mrs C S Sargent).

Liriodendron chinense (Magnoliaceae)

Very similar to the more commonly grown tulip tree, *Liriodendron tulipifera*, from North America, but with leaves which are bluer green beneath and which have a narrower constriction in the middle. It is an accommodating tree which will grow in any soil provided it is not too poor. The leaves turn a beautiful yellow in autumn.

'Formerly this tree was very abundant on the Lushan mountains in the neighborhood of Kiukiang', Wilson wrote, 'but all the large trees have been cut down and only odd specimens and dense bushes remain . . . A colloquial name in Hupeh is "Wo-chang-chin" = Goose-foot, which has reference to the shape of the leaves'.[5]

Lonicera (Caprifoliaceae)

Honeysuckles

Wilson introduced thirteen different honeysuckles, some of them shrubs and some climbers. *Lonicera tragophylla* is one of the climbers, a most spectacular one with bright yellow flowers larger (6–9 cm long) than those of the other climbing species, and borne in clusters of ten to twenty in May and June. The only disadvantage is that the flowers are unscented, but this should not dissuade one from growing it, for it is a most beautiful species with the advantage of being happy in a shady position.

Two of the shrubby species, closely related to each other, which Wilson introduced are the evergreen or semi-evergreen *L. nitida* and *L. pileata*. They are grown more for their small, glossy leaves than for their flowers and fruit, which are not especially conspicuous. *Lonicera nitida* is particularly good for hedging, being fast-growing (up to 3 metres) and amenable to clipping. A popular form with yellow leaves is 'Baggesen's Gold', which can be found in most garden centres, and the most commonly sold form, with dark green leaves, has been named 'Ernest Wilson'. *Lonicera pileata* is somewhat similar, but does not grow so tall and has a more spreading habit: it is relatively salt-tolerant and therefore a good species for seaside planting.

Magnolia (Magnoliaceae)

Wilson introduced seven of these beautiful trees into cultivation. One of the most attractive is the species named after him, *M. wilsonii* (colour pl. 11). It is a small, deciduous tree growing to 7.5 metres tall. The white, cup-shaped, fragrant flowers, 7–10 cm across, are produced after the leaves have appeared, and are downward-facing, unlike the more familiar spring-flowering magnolias such as *M. stellata*, *M. sargentiana* or *M.* × *soulangiana*. Often there is a second flush of flowers in late summer. The stamens are deep red or crimson-purple, and the seeds are bright red. It grows best in shade or semi-shade. Double-flowered forms have been reported – one grows at Wakehurst Place in Sussex. Wilson commented in *Plantae Wilsonianae* that 'In late May and early June it is very conspicuous with its pure white petals and sepals and bright red stamens and carpels. It is very floriferous and fragrant and promises to be a welcome addition to the list of cultivated plants.'[6]

The other magnolias introduced by Wilson are *M. dawsoniana*, *M. delavayi*, *M. officinalis*, *M. sargentiana* and its variety *robusta*, *M. sinensis* and *M. sprengeri*. Of *M. officinalis* Wilson wrote, '*Magnolia officinalis* is very commonly cultivated on the mountains of western Hupeh and Szech'uan, but we have not met with a spontaneous tree in the forests . . . its bark and flower-buds constitute a valued drug which is exported in quantity from central and western China to all parts of the Empire. It is for its bark and flower-buds that the tree is cultivated. The removal of the bark causes the death of the tree and this would account for its disappearance from the forest.'[7] He considered that *M. sargentiana* was 'one of the noblest of its family.'[8] All the plants of *M. sprengeri* 'Diva' (colour pl. 19) in cultivation are derived from seed which Wilson sent to J C Williams at Caerhays Castle in Cornwall.

Malus hupehensis (Rosaceae)

This species was first introduced under the name *M. theifera*. It is a small, stiffly branched tree with fragrant white flowers which open from pink buds in April or May. The small fruits are deep red. It is common in west and central China, where forms with white and rose-pink flowers grow together. '[It] is very beautiful in spring when covered with light pink flowers,' Rehder wrote, 'and resembles at this time a flowering Cherry rather than an Apple tree; the effect of the flowers is heightened by the purple calyx and the purplish tints of the unfolding leaves.'[9] In gardens, the pink-flowered form is given the name *M. hupehensis* forma *rosea*. Wilson also sent back *M. prattii*, *M. toringoides* and *M. yunnanensis*, all of which have good autumn colour.

Meconopsis (Papaveraceae)

The yellow poppywort, *M. integrifolia* (colour pl. 1), is one of Wilson's most famous introductions and one of the most beautiful. The yellow flowers can measure up to

15 cm across and possess between six and eight petals. The leaves are covered with pale brown hairs. The flowering stem rises from a rosette of basal leaves and can bear as many as ten flowers. Its wild distribution is one of the most wide-ranging of the genus (from Tibet through China to northern Burma), and it is a rather variable species, varying in habit, degree and hairiness, flower shape and presence or absence of a style.

Meconopsis integrifolia is monocarpic, i.e. the plant dies after it has flowered. Luckily it produces abundant seed. It is rather fussy about its growing conditions, hating both a waterlogged soil or one which is too dry, nor does it like much sun.

The other species of *Meconopsis* which Wilson found was *M. punicea*. In 1934 Sir George Taylor (eminent botanist and plant collector, and Director of the Royal Botanic Gardens, Kew from 1956 to 1971) published a monograph of *Meconopsis*, where he wrote of *M. punicea* 'No species has drawn such superlative and almost extravagant epithets as *M. punicea*. Those who have had the privilege of seeing the species in its natural habitat, where it brightens the copses and meadows with splashes of the most vivid colour, are unanimous in their eulogies, and one feels from the descriptions that the ecstatic joy of a first acquaintance with the plant is warranted.'[10]

It first flowered in cultivation in 1904. Its solitary, brilliant red, drooping flowers, up to 10 cm long, are unique in *Meconopsis*. Cultivation is not easy – the seed is difficult to germinate and the plants usually die after they have produced flowers – the reason for this is not understood. It is therefore very important to save seed so that new plants can be raised.

Parthenocissus henryana (Vitaceae)

A beautiful deciduous climber (colour pl. 15) which clings to its support by means of tendrils which end in sticky pads. The leaves have three to five dark green or bronze leaflets which have the veins picked out in white. Before they fall in the autumn, the leaves turn crimson-red. After a hot summer, dark blue fruits will be produced.

It was discovered by Augustine Henry, after whom it was named, in about 1885, but not introduced until 1900, when Wilson brought it back from central China.

Picea (Pinaceae)

Spruces

A genus of ornamental evergreen conifers, rather similar to *Abies* and requiring similar cultivation. *Picea brachytyla* is a rather variable species which Wilson introduced several times. The branches ascend but the branchlets droop, giving a most attractive effect. The upper surface of the needles is bright green, in contrast to the undersurface, which is white.

A Japanese species which Wilson introduced in 1914 is *P. koyamae*, with dark brown peeling bark and cones about 10 cm long. More spectacular, especially when covered in pinkish-red, young cones and crimson male flowers in April and May, is

P. likiangensis, which is not grown as commonly as it should be. Young cones are upright, but as they mature they turn over and hang from the branches. This spruce is not one to plant in old age, for the display of cones will only begin when the tree is about twenty-five years old! *Picea wilsonii* has smaller cones (which remain on the tree for a long time), and the young shoots are attractively white.

Primula (Primulaceae)

One of the most popular 'candelabra' primulas in cultivation is *P. pulverulenta* (colour pl. 17), which Wilson introduced from China in 1903. The plant has several whorls of purple-eyed crimson flowers borne on white-mealy stems up to 90 cm tall in June and July. To grow well, it must be given plenty of moisture; indeed it is at its best planted in boggy soil at the edge of a pond or stream, and is happy in either sun or shade. Drifts of this primula make a lovely feature in a water-garden.

Plants are not long-lived, but produce abundant seed, so self-sown seedlings will perpetuate the species. In cultivation, it has been crossed with other 'candelabras' to produce a colourful range of hybrids which enjoy similar growing conditions.

Other primulas which Wilson introduced are the fiery orange-flowered *P. cockburniana*, *P. vittata* (now called *P. secundiflora*) and *P. polyneura*, whose yellow-eyed flowers vary from pale pink to deep red-purple.

Prunus (Rosaceae)

Wilson was very interested in the flowering cherries and introduced some fourteen or so from his various expeditions. Perhaps the best are *P. conradinae* and *P. serrula*. *Prunus conradinae* is an elegant small tree, which produces abundant white or pinkish flowers on leafless twigs in February. *Prunus serrula* is often grown for its beautiful, shiny, red-brown bark, which peels as it ages. The leaves are narrow and the white flowers appear in April. In 1900 Wilson introduced *P. serrulata* var. *hupehensis* (sometimes called var. *spontanea*), which is thought to be an ancestor of the flowering cherry – it has double white flowers and is commonly grown in gardens and as a street tree. It is particularly pretty with its bronzy young leaves, and bright autumn colour.

Rheum alexandrae (Polygonaceae)

An unusual rhubarb (colour pl. 16), with a flowering stem which grows to 1.3 metres tall, the flowers enveloped in pale yellowish bracts, which become tinged with red as they mature. It will grow in sun or semi-shade and needs a rather moist soil. It should be grown more often, for it always attracts attention.

Rhododendron (Ericaceae)

One of the most important cultivated shrubby genera and one of the biggest, with some 850 species as well as numerous hybrids which have been bred over the last 150 years. Rhododendrons are grown for their often spectacular flowers which occur in every colour except true blue. They vary from dwarf plants suitable for the rock-garden to small trees reaching a height of 13 metres. Wilson introduced over sixty species; only George Forrest, who also collected in China, introduced more. Some of the best are mentioned below.

Rhododendron calophytum can grow to 15 metres tall and bears trusses of white or pale pink flowers, each with a deep crimson basal blotch. It needs to be sheltered both from wind and from excessive sun. Rehder and Wilson wrote that 'The bark is cinnamon-red passing to pale brown with age. The long scarlet pedicels add greatly to the beauty of the flowers which are borne in large loose trusses'.[11]

Rhododendron davidsonianum produces its pale pink flowers, 2–3.3 cm long, in April. Its leaves are a dark, glossy green above and densely brown-scaly beneath. The new growth is often purplish red. Wilson named it after 'Dr W Henry Davidson, of the Friends Foreign Mission, at Chengtu Fu, western Szech'uan, in grateful recognition of the important services which he rendered to me after my serious accident in the autumn of 1910'.[12]

Rhododendron fargesii (colour pl. 3) was named after the French missionary Père Farges, who found it in the early 1890s. Wilson introduced it from Hubei in 1901. The plant grows to over 3 metres and the flowers vary from pale pink to purplish pink and are produced in great abundance in March and April.

Introduced as *R. primulinum*, the small-leaved *R. flavidum* produces primrose-yellow, funnel-shaped flowers in March and April. It grows up to a metre high and was introduced from Sichuan in 1905.

Rhododendron lutescens also has yellow flowers but is a taller plant, 1–2 or more metres tall, and the branches have lovely smooth, brown flaking bark. The new growth is an attractive reddish brown. This species flowers from February until April and the early flowers can be damaged by frost unless it is grown in a sheltered place.

Rhododendron moupinense is a dwarf shrub which was first found by Père David (of *Davidia* fame) and introduced in 1909. The beautiful white or pink flowers, one to three together at the ends of the twigs, appear as early as February and so are liable to frost damage. 'This species is usually found growing upon evergreen oaks and other broad-leaved trees' Rehder and Wilson wrote.[13]

Another of Père David's discoveries, *R. orbiculare* (colour pl. 20) covers itself every spring in beautiful magenta-pink, bell-shaped flowers up to 4 cm long. The scientific name refers to its leaves, which are almost round.[14]

Growing to about 1.5 metres and densely branched, *R. williamsianum* bears rose-red bell-shaped flowers in April. It can be slow-growing, but produces flowers when young. It should be grown in a sunny place where the plants will be neat and hemispherical. This species was named after J C Williams of Caerhays Castle, Cornwall, who Wilson described as 'the first amateur to appreciate the horticultural value of the Rhododendrons of western China; in his garden the best collection of these new introductions is to be found.'[15]

In 1926, the Royal Horticultural Society and the Rhododendron Society awarded the Loder Cup to Wilson for his *Rhododendron* introductions.

Rosa (Rosaceae)

Roses

We are so used to growing roses in our gardens that it is hard to imagine life without them. Roses are found all round the temperate zone of the northern hemisphere and the first to be grown were European and Near Eastern species. Later, roses from the New World and the Far East were introduced, and subsequent hybridisation produced the modern classes of roses, such as 'Large-flowered' and 'Cluster-flowered', which we now cultivate.

Some eighteen roses were introduced into gardens by Wilson, including the climbing *R. helenae*, named after his wife; *R. murieliae*, named after his daughter; and *R. sinowilsonii*, named in allusion to his nickname, 'Chinese' Wilson. One of his most spectacular introductions was *R. filipes*, which can grow to 9 metres and produces single, white, fragrant flowers in huge clusters up to 30 cm across. It looks best when allowed to climb into a sturdy tree. *Rosa moyesii* (colour pl. 12) was introduced in 1903 – it is a shrub 2–3.5 metres tall and bears single, pink to blood-red flowers 4–6.5 cm across followed by orange-red, bottle-shaped hips. Rehder and Wilson wrote, 'The flowers vary considerably in colour . . . The typical form, which has dark red flowers, is abundant in the upland thickets round Tachien-lu and is one of the most beautiful of Roses'.[16] Wilson introduced *R. omiensis* (now called *R. sericea* var. *omiensis*) from Emei Shan (known to Wilson as 'Mt Omei'). It is unusual in that the white flowers generally have four petals rather than the five which are normal in single roses.

Among the other roses which Wilson sent to the West are *R. banksiopsis*, *R. corymbulosa*, *R. davidii*, *R. multibracteata*, *R. rubus*, *R. setipoda* and *R. willmottiae*.

Sorbus (Rosaceae)

There are some 120 species of *Sorbus* – perhaps the best known are *S. aucuparia*, the rowan or mountain ash, and *S. aria*, the whitebeam, both of which are British natives. In gardens, many introduced species are grown for their bunches of colourful berries, which follow the clusters of whitish flowers. Wilson sent back twelve species from his Chinese trips, of which the most commonly grown are *S. hupehensis* (colour pl. 7) and *S. prattii*, both of which have white berries, those of the former being attractively flushed with pink. He also introduced *Sorbus megalocarpa* with brownish fruit which are large for the genus (more than 3 cm long) and handsome foliage, *Sorbus scalaris*, a red-fruited species with pretty, fern-like leaves and *S. sargentiana*, which produces enormous bunches of up to 500 orange-red fruits. In addition to the beautiful fruits, these species are worth growing for their fine autumn colour.

Styrax (Styracaceae)

Only a handful of the 120 species of *Styrax* are cultivated. They are northern hemisphere trees and shrubs which are known as 'snowbells' in North America because of their white, hanging, bell-shaped flowers up to 2 cm long. They will not grow in limy soil. Wilson was responsible for introducing three of the Chinese species to the West, namely *S. dasyantha*, *S. hemsleyana* and *S. wilsonii*. *Styrax hemsleyana* is the hardiest; the other two species require a sheltered position.

Taiwania cryptomerioides (Taxodiaceae)

A rare conifer which Wilson introduced from Mount Morrison in Taiwan in 1920. It is a tall, conical tree, growing to 60 metres in the wild, but less in cultivation. The bark is reddish brown and the small cones are only 11–13 mm long, borne at the ends of the branches. In gardens it needs shelter and a site which never dries out.

Thalictrum delavayi (Ranunculaceae)

Introduced from western China under the name *T. dipterocarpum*, this is one of the more attractive thalictrums, growing to over a metre tall and producing dainty lilac-pink flowers, each with a bunch of cream stamens. It is a useful plant for a herbaceous border or for planting among shrubs.

Viburnum (Caprifoliaceae)

Some twenty different viburnums are in cultivation thanks to Wilson. The genus contains over 150 species of small trees or shrubs, some of which are deciduous, and others evergreen. Perhaps his best introductions are *V. betulifolium* (colour pl. 6), *V. cinnamonifolium*, *V. foetidum*, *V. hupehense*, *V. davidii* and *V. rhytidophyllum* of which the last-named is particularly striking. It is a most handsome evergreen with big, glossy, wrinkled leaves which are grey-felty beneath. Small, white flowers are produced in May in flat clusters and these are followed by red berries which finally turn black. *Viburnum davidii* bears turquoise-blue berries and the fruits of *V. cinnamonifolium* are blue-black. If you want red fruits, then grow *V. betulifolium*, *V. foetidum* or *V. hupehense*. A slight problem with viburnums is that many plants are self-incompatible i.e. they will not set seed if grown on their own. It is necessary to plant two or more plants together, preferably from different clones. Viburnums are generally easy to grow and require a rich soil which does not dry out.

Notes and References

Unless otherwise stated, all books and articles cited are by Ernest H Wilson.

Sources of unpublished material

AA	Archives of the Arnold Arboretum, Boston, Massachusetts
Kew	Archives of the Library of The Royal Botanic Gardens, Kew
pers. papers	Personal papers of Ernest H Wilson in the possession of his nephew Mr Frank Wilson and his granddaughter Mrs Barbara Abbot (née Wilson-Slate)

Foreword

1   E I Farrington *Ernest H Wilson, Plant Hunter*. Boston, Massachusetts: The Stratford Company

2   D J Foley *The Flowering World of 'Chinese Wilson'*. Toronto: Collier-Macmillan Canada Ltd

3   There have of course been numerous references to Wilson's work in gardening dictionaries, books on plant hunting and in journals over the years, but the only modern accounts featuring new information on Wilson are in *Arnoldia*, published by the Arnold Arboretum at Harvard University. Three issues in particular (36, 5 September/October 1976); 40, 3 (May/June 1980); and 40/4 (July/August 1980) review and assess Wilson's achievements as a photographer and a botanist. Another detailed reference appears in Stephen Spongberg's *A Reunion of Trees*, published by Harvard University Press (Cambridge, Massachusetts) in 1990.

Introduction

1   Farrington *Ernest H Wilson*, p 96

2   Peter J Veitch, great-great-nephew of Sir Harry Veitch, the head of the firm in Wilson's time, told me that papers that had remained in family hands had been destroyed earlier this century.

3   According to Wilson's granddaughter Barbara Abbott, the letters were destroyed by Muriel Wilson after the death of her parents.

4   Journal entry for 5 July 1910. (See *A Naturalist in Western China* (1913), vol 1, p 82, and Wilson's diary for 4 June–4 August 1910 'Expedition to Sungpan' (AA).)

5   Published as 'Leaves from my Chinese notebook' between 1905 and 1906 (vols 37–9)

6   Letter dated 24 November 1909 (pers. papers)

7   'She liked neither America nor the Americans' according to a biography of the Director of the Arboretum (S B Sutton *Charles Sprague Sargent and the Arnold Arboretum*, (Harvard University Press, Cambridge, Massachusetts, 1970), p 250).

8   Letter to his mother dated 5 February 1914 (pers. papers)

9   Extract from Wilson's accounts for the period 7 April to 21 June 1903 (AA). The exchange rate in 1903 was seventy-two Hankow taels to US$100.

10   The contract with his 'Boy-Cook', for example, reads:

1. This is to certify that the undersigned agrees to accompany Mr E H Wilson, in the capacity of Boy-Cook and general servant, anywhere and everywhere during the period of the latter's stay in China or for as long as the said Mr E H Wilson desires.

2. Mr E H Wilson reserves the right to discharge the said Boy on payment of wages and passage money to the port of Ichang. But should dismissal be necessitated by misconduct, insubordination or any unlawful act Mr E H Wilson's liabilities in regard to passage money and wages to the port of Ichang cease at the moment the said Boy is discharged.

3. Wages at the rate of twenty dollars per month will be paid to the said Boy. When travelling over land rice money, not exceeding Taels four per month will be allowed. In the passage up river and whilst living in Boat in any town no such allowance will be made.

4. Mr E H Wilson engages himself, if he is wholly satisfied with the conduct and work of the said Boy, to present the latter with three months wages (sixty dollars) gratuity on their return to Ichang.

5. On and after the signing of this mutual agreement the services of the said Boy are entirely and wholly at the use of Mr E H Wilson.

6. Mutually agreed upon and signed this the twenty-fourth February 1904.
(AA)

11   Letter to C S Sargent dated 11 February 1907 (AA)

12   Journal entry for 12 June 1903 (AA)

13   *Plant Hunting* (1927), vol 1, p xxv

14   Farrington *Ernest H Wilson*, p 96

15   His son-in-law George Slate apparently described him to his daughter Barbara as 'the worst of Victorian fathers'. She remembers hearing her mother describing how she was once beaten for walking home from school in the company of a boy. The job to which Wilson objected was the post of librarian at the Massachusetts Horticultural Society, where in fact Muriel met her future husband. A trustee of the society, Wilson had some influence on its affairs but failed in this instance to have his way.

16   *Plant Hunting*, vol 1, p ix–x

17   Among the more important examples listed by Rehder, Wilson's colleague at the Arnold Arboretum, are *Aconitum wilsonii* (now *A. carmichaelii* var *wilsonii*), *Aesculus wilsonii, Aralia wilsonii, Cladastris wilsonii, Corydalis wilsonii, Daphne wilsonii,* (now *D. tangutica*), *Deutzia* × *wilsonii, Euonymus wilsonii, Ilex wilsonii, Iris wilsonii, Magnolia wilsonii, Populus wilsonii, Sophora wilsonii* (now *S. prazeri* var. *wilsonii*), *Sorbus wilsoniana, Spiraea wilsonii, Styrax wilsonii, Ulmus wilsoniana* and *Viburnum wilsonii*. (See A Rehder 'Ernest Henry Wilson' in *Journal of the Arnold Arboretum*, xi (1930), pp 181–92)

18   *The Hillier Manual of Trees and Shrubs* (Newton Abbot, David & Charles, 5th edn 1972 (reprinted 1989)), p 364

Chapter 1

1   These records have been preserved at the new school which has been built not far from the original site.

2   *Aristocrats of the Trees* (1930), p 131

3   This examination was administered by the 'Department of Science and Art' and held annually at centres throughout England. Candidates were able to take courses in science from a list of twenty-five on offer. The examinations were of two kinds – a 'Class' examination and an Honours examination. The Class examination could be taken at Elementary or Advanced level. The Honours examination was of a more advanced character. The Queen's Prize was a scholarship which Wilson used to continue his studies after he had left Birmingham. He took part 1 of the Honours examination in 1898 and presumably would have gone on to take part 2 the following year.

4   There seems to have been some disagreement about the role that Henry's work played in arousing the Veitches' interest in Chinese plants. Wilson wrote in the *Gardeners' Chronicle* that 'the attention of Messrs Veitch of Chelsea became drawn to the mass of materials Henry had collected,' and that 'The result of this was that they applied to the Director of Kew to nominate a likely collector' (*Gardeners' Chronicle* 37 (June 1905), p 337), but James Herbert Veitch was anxious to correct him. In a letter to Wilson he wrote:

'You are, however, wrong in one little point, but I do not wish it publicly contradicted. It was not Henry's specimens which drew our attention to China. When I was in Japan in '91, '92 and '93 I was quite aware there was a very rich field, and so was Sargent, with whom I was some time in Japan. In fact I wrote home here to my Chief [Harry James Veitch] to know whether I might not go (and I have the letters now) but my Chief very promptly sat on it, I did not go, and the matter dropped.

For years I had been pressing the matter, and though Henry's work gave a fillip to my wishes, the expedition was long determined on in my own mind, before Henry appeared on the scene.'
(Letter dated 2 June 1905 (AA))

5   One of the leading experts in this field at the time was the Arnold Arboretum's chief propagator Jackson Dawson.

6   Letter dated 30 March 1899 (AA)

7   *Aristocrats of the Garden* (1917), p 275. Curiously the agreement Wilson signed for this trip (dated 27 March 1899) contains no such instructions. He may have been confusing the instructions he was given for this expedition with those set out for his second expedition to China for the Veitches, which specified that he

collect in 'that district determined in conversation with James H Veitch' and 'in that district spend the Autumn of 1903 and the Spring, Summer and Autumn of 1904' (Instructions for the second Veitch expedition, dated 8 December 1902 (AA)). Alternatively it may be that Wilson was not above the use of a little literary licence in making an account more interesting for the reader.

By the time of Wilson's first expedition to China, Henry had been posted a number of times within the customs service. In 1898 he took up appointment as acting chief commissioner of customs at Simao.

8   At this time Cunard had several liners in commission which had two or three times the *Pavonia*'s capacity and more than twice her speed.

9   The fare, travelling saloon-class, would have been about £12.

10   *Harvard Graduates' Magazine* XXXV (1927), p 614

11   *Aristocrats of the Garden*, p 276

12   The consular service issued safe-conduct documents to bona-fide British nationals wishing to travel through parts of inland China. These were often large and impressive affairs, liberally endorsed with official stamps. Written in Chinese, they would identify the traveller and give the purpose of the mission. A warning not to interfere in any way with the bearer on pain of severe punishment would be given, and an assurance that the traveller would deal with the Chinese people fairly and cause no harm.

13   *Aristocrats of the Garden*, pp 281–2

14   Ibid.

15   *Aristocrats of the Garden*, p 293

16   Ibid., p 284

17   Letter dated 17 May 1900 (AA)

18   Letter dated 16 February 1900 (AA)

19   Letter dated 28 June 1907 (AA). The 'driers' were sheets of absorbent paper used in the plant presses. According to Dr Shui-Ying Hu (*Arnoldia* 40, 4 (July/August 1980), p 168), these materials were not available in China at this time and it is probable that Wilson brought them with him.

20   *Aristocrats of the Garden*, p 287

21   The transliteration given for this name, and for *yang-tao* (kiwi fruit), below, follows Wilson's spelling.

22   *Aristocrats of the Garden*, p 289

23   Ibid., pp 290–1

24   From this first batch of seed, collected in November 1900, more than 13,000 trees were raised.

25   Wilson describes them as similar to a walnut but somewhat smaller and 'as hard as flint and absolutely unbreakable' (*Aristocrats of the Garden*, p 292).

26   Ibid.

27   Both Ernest and Nellie's ages are shown as twenty-eight on their marriage certificate. In fact Ernest was twenty-six and Nellie was thirty.

Chapter 2

Note: the *Gardeners' Chronicle* articles cited here are all from the series Wilson called 'Leaves from my Chinese notebook'.

1   *Gardeners' Chronicle* 37 (June 1905), p 382

2   This important plant was introduced to Britain in about 1820 by John Reeves the elder. Wilson records (*Gardeners' Chronicle* 37 (June 1905), p 382) that it is found in great abundance on the limestone cliffs of the Yichang gorges.

3   *Gardeners' Chronicle* 37 (June 1905), p 382. The names of the rapids given in this part of the story reflect Wilson's spellings.

4   Ibid., 38 (July 1905), p 4

5   Ibid., p 24

6   W C Haines-Watson had accompanied Wilson on his first trip to Songpan in 1903. Wilson named *Rhododendron watsonii* after him (see *Bulletin of Miscellaneous Information, Kew* (1910), p 112.

7   Insect white wax is made from a secretion produced by insects belonging to the scale insect family (*Coccidae*), and is used in the manufacture of candles and for sizing paper and cotton goods. Wilson devotes a whole chapter of *A Naturalist in Western China* (1913) to this product. For a modern account of the industry, see Roy Lancaster, *Roy Lancaster Travels in China* (Antique Collectors' Club, Woodbridge, 1989), pp 321–3.

8   Letter dated 29 September 1903 (Kew)

9   *Gardeners' Chronicle* 38 (December 1905), p 420

10   Ibid., p 422

11   Ibid., p 459

12   Ibid., 39 (January 1906), p 12

13   During the time that Wilson was travelling in China, the border was ill-defined and contested. Mutual borders were not agreed until the Anglo-Tibetan Agreement of 1914.

14   Captain Gill's book, *River of Golden Sand*, was the definitive work on China at this time.

15   *Gardeners' Chronicle* 39 (March 1906), p 165

16   Ibid., p 139

17   Notes for lecture given on 28 February 1928 (pers. papers)

18   *Gardeners' Chronicle* 39 (June 1906), p 402

19   *Naturalist in W China*, vol 1, p 144

20   *Gardeners' Chronicle* 39 (June 1906), p 402

21   Ibid.

22   Notes for lecture given on 28 February 1928 (pers. papers)

23   *Gardeners' Chronicle* 38 (November 1905), p 355

24   Ibid.

25   Ibid., 39 (April 1906), p 258

26   The 'Norfolk Howards' Wilson refers to are bed bugs (named after Joshua Bug, who changed his name to Norfolk Howard, only to become the butt of popular humour).

27   Letter dated 8 October 1904 (Kew)

28   Letter dated 2 December 1903 (AA)

29   *Gardeners' Chronicle* 37 (February 1905), p 114

30   Letter dated 2 December 1903 (AA)

31   See R A Howard 'E H Wilson as a botanist' in *Arnoldia* 40, 3 (May/June 1980). Each sample of seed or specimen of plant material collected was assigned its own unique number. This number corresponded with an entry in a ledger written at the same time. Careful numbering of materials ensured accurate cataloguing of collections after Wilson returned home.

Chapter 3

1   This was a violet-coloured primrose. Unfortunately it did not prove hardy and was later lost to cultivation.

2   Letter to C S Sargent dated 4 October 1906 (AA)

3   Letter dated 14 September 1906 (AA)

4   Letter dated 6 November 1906 (AA)

5   See Peter J Chvany 'E H Wilson, Photographer' in *Arnoldia* 36, 5 (September/October 1976), pp 181–236

6   Letter dated 11 February 1907 (AA)

7   Letter dated 19 June 1918 (AA). Meyer's body was recovered from the Yangtze in June 1918.

8   *Naturalist in W China*, vol 2, pp 151–2

9   According to Rehder's obituary of Wilson (*Journal of the Arnold Arboretum*, 11 (1930), pp 181–92), his first publication was in fact an article entitled 'Western China, a field for the sportsman' in *The Field* (*The Field* CVI (1905), 109).

10   *Naturalist in W China*, vol 2, p 178

11   *The Lilies of Eastern Asia* (Dulau & Co, London, 1925), pp 99–100

12   He was to succeed in collecting bulbs of this species in Taiwan in 1918 (ibid., p 78).

13   Chengdu is the city of Sin-din-fu described in early editions of Marco Polo's *Travels*.

14   *Naturalist in W China*, vol 1, p 171

15   Food in China was often difficult to obtain and Wilson and his men were forced to resort to that much cursed navy ration, the ships' biscuit.

16   *Naturalist in W China*, vol 1, p 178

17   Ibid., p 187

18   A coolie's daily wage would have been about 150 cash.

19   *Naturalist in W China*, vol 1, p 196

20   Ibid., p 198

21 Ibid., p 233
22 Ibid., p 241
23 Ibid., p 243
24 Letter dated 21 November 1908 (AA)
25 Letter dated 9 March 1909 (AA)

Chapter 4

1   *Naturalist in W China*, vol 1, p 28
2   Ibid., p 122
3   Ibid., p 38
4   Ibid., p 48
5   Ibid., p 69
6   Ibid., p 60
7   Ibid., p 98
8   Ibid., p 96
9   A tael was equivalent to $1\frac{1}{3}$ oz of silver and was worth 1.38 Szechwan dollars at this time.
10 *Naturalist in W China*, vol 1 p 119
11 See Frank Kingdon Ward *In the Land of the Blue Poppy* (Cambridge University Press, 1913), pp 12–14
12 *Naturalist in W China*, vol 1, p 40
13 *Plant Hunting*, vol 2, p 149
14 Ibid., pp 150–1
15 Farrington *Ernest H Wilson*, p xviii
16 *Plant Hunting*, vol 2, p 144
17 Ibid., p 152
18 Letter dated 10 September 1910 (AA)
19 Letter dated 4 December 1910 (AA)
20 Ibid.
21 Letter dated 16 December 1910 (Kew)
22 Letter dated 28 January 1911 (AA)
23 Wilson had in fact introduced this plant to England in 1903, when he shipped 300 bulbs to Messrs Veitch. These bulbs were distributed under the erroneous name of *Lilium myriophyllum*, however, and the mistake was not discovered until 1913.

Chapter 5

1   'It was very good of Hong Kong, and I fully appreciate the honour, but my injured leg, agreement with Harvard, and above all, the strong desire I have to settle down near Kew prevented my accepting the offer. Eight years ago I should have taken it with pleasure but since then I have had a pretty full experience of the Far

East,' Wilson wrote to Colonel Prain, Director of the Royal Botanic Gardens, Kew. (Letter dated 16 December 1910 (Kew))

2   Only twelve articles appear under Wilson's name, compared with forty-four attributed to Rehder. A further forty-seven articles were written jointly.

3   Letter to his mother dated 15 December 1912 (pers. papers)

4   This is the Society's highest award. When it was first instituted in 1897 there were sixty recipients, increased to sixty-three by the time Queen Victoria died.

5   Letter dated 14 December 1913 (pers. papers)

6   Letter dated 1 January 1914 (pers. papers)

7   Letter dated 5 February 1914 (pers. papers)

8   These investigations in Japan would form the basis of his definitive work *The Cherries of Japan* (Cambridge, Massachusetts: The University Press, 1916 (Arnold Arboretum Publication No 7)).

9   Letter to his mother dated 8 September 1914 (pers. papers)

10   *The Conifers and Taxads of Japan* (The University Press, Cambridge, Massachusetts, 1916 (Arnold Arboretum Publication No 8)), p v

11   Letter to Professor R S Cocks dated 12 May 1915 (AA)

12   Letter dated 17 July 1915 (pers. papers)

13   Letter dated 18 October 1915 (pers. papers)

14   This was a prestigious award. The medal was struck in gold and had a face value of US$300 in 1915.

15   Letter to C S Sargent dated 21 March 1917 (AA)

16   Ibid.

17   See 'The Bonin Islands and their ligneous vegetation' and 'New woody plants from the Bonin Islands' in *Journal of the Arnold Arboretum* 1919–20, pp 97–115 and 115–21

18   Letter to his mother dated 23 March 1917 (pers. papers)

19   *Plant Hunting*, vol 2, p 207

20   Known as Quelpaert when Wilson visited it.

21   *Plant Hunting*, vol 2, p 173

22   Ibid., p 175

23   Ibid., p 169

24   Ibid., p 232

25   Kijiro Akashi had in fact exhibited thirty varieties of the Kurume azaleas at the Panama Pacific Exposition at San Francisco in 1915, but none of these specimens was successfully cultivated in the United States. Wilson's collection of Kurume azaleas was established at the Royal Horticultural Society's gardens at Wisley in 1947 and have been grown there ever since as the 'Wilson Fifty'.

26   Letter dated 21 June 1918 (pers. papers)

27   *Plant Hunting*, vol 2, p 179

28   Ibid., p 180

29   Ibid., p 182

Chapter 6

1 See Peter J Chvany 'E H Wilson, Photographer' in *Arnoldia* 36, 5 (September/October 1976), p 230. The exchange rate at this time was about US$5 to the pound.

2 H Morrison 'Report on inspection work at the Arnold Arboretum' (unpublished), 1921 (AA)

3 Letter dated 17 September 1920 (AA)

4 Letter dated 19 October 1920 (AA)

5 *Western Mail* (Australia), 25 November 1920

6 Ibid.

7 *Sydney Morning Herald*, 20 January 1921

8 *Creswick Advertiser*, 22 April 1921

9 *Wellington Evening Post*, 11 March 1921

10 Letter dated 28 March 1921 (AA)

11 *Daily Standard* (Australia), 3 June 1921

12 Letter to C S Sargent dated 31 October 1921 (AA)

13 Ibid.

14 Ibid.

15 Ibid.

16 *Plant Hunting*, vol 1, p 73

17 Ibid., p 77

18 Ibid., p 79

19 Ibid., p 84

20 Ibid.

21 Ibid., p 79

22 Ibid., p 87. It is interesting that Wilson uses the same anglicised version of the native name for the falls as H H Johnston in his book on the life of Livingstone published in 1891. Wilson's translation is far more vivid, however; Johnstone has merely 'Smoke sounds there'.

23 Notes for a lecture to the Colony Club, New York, given on 28 February 1928 (pers. papers)

Chapter 7

1 *Aristocrats of the Garden*, p xxii

2 'what the immediate future of the AA will be no one can tell . . . Having in view the altered financial condition of the Arnold Arboretum it is my duty to ask you to leave China and return here with the best possible speed,' Wilson wrote to Rock. (Letter dated 11 April 1927 (AA))

3 *Aristocrats of the Trees*, p 1

4 The dedication reads 'To Bob-O-Link'. 'Bob-O-Link' (shortened by the family to 'Bob') was Wilson's nickname for Betty Mumford.

5   *Plant Hunting*, vol 2, pp 11–12

6   Muriel Wilson was anxious that her parents' remains should be buried in 'British soil'.

7   A plaque attached to the monument states that it was erected by: the Arnold Arboretum; the Horticultural Club of Boston; the Horticultural Society of New York; the Jardin Botanique de Montréal; the Kew Guild; the Massachusetts Horticultural Society; the Pennsylvania Horticultural Society; the Royal Botanic Gardens, Kew; the Royal Horticultural Society; the Society of China and the Société Botanique de France. The quotation in the inscription is attributed to vol 145 (1919) of *Curtis's Botanical Magazine*, which was dedicated to Wilson.

Chapter 8

1   E H M Cox *Plant-hunting in China* (Collins, London, 1945), p 136

2   C S Sargent (ed.) *Plantae Wilsonianae*. Cambridge, Massachusetts, The University Press.

3   Ibid., vol 2, p 458

4   Ibid., vol 1, p 333

5   Ibid., p 410

6   Ibid., p 396

7   Ibid., p 392

8   Ibid., p 398

9   Ibid., vol 2, p 284

10   G Taylor *An Account of the Genus Meconopsis* (New Flora and Silva, London, 1934), p 55

11   *Plantae Wilsonianae*, vol 1, p 544

12   Ibid., p 515. For an account of Wilson's accident, see chapter 4 of this book.

13   Ibid., p 525

14   Rehder and Wilson commented that 'the leaves of this species which resemble those of a small-leaved Nuphar are remarkably distinct.' (Ibid., p 540)

15   Ibid., p 538

16   Ibid., vol 2, p 325

Wilson's Plant Hunting and Gardening Books

A Naturalist in Western China, 1913. (Reprinted in paperback by Cadogan Books (London), 1986).

Aristocrats of the Garden, 1917. (Last reprinted by Williams & Norgate (London), 1938.)

The Romance of Our Trees, Doubleday Page & Co (Garden City, New York), 1920.

Plant Hunting, The Stratford Company (Boston, Massachusetts), 1927). (Volume 1 reprinted as *Smoke that Thunders* by Waterstone & Co (London), 1985.)

More Aristocrats of the Garden, The Stratford Company, 1928.

China, Mother of Gardens, The Stratford Company, 1929.

Aristocrats of the Trees, 1930. (Reprinted in paperback by Dover Publications Inc (New York), 1974.)

If I were to Make a Garden, The Stratford Company, 1931. (Published posthumously, this book is mainly a collection of articles first published in the American magazine *House and Garden*, with a foreword by Wilson's friend Richardson Wright, editor of *House and Garden* at the time of his death.)

Chinese Place Names

With the exception of a few well-known names (Peking, the Yangtze River), the spelling of Chinese place names used in the main text of this book generally follows the modern system of transcribing Chinese known as pinyin. Wilson's own writings use a mixture of systems that were in use earlier this century, and to the non-specialist these spellings may look very different from the pinyin versions. The following list shows the pinyin versions of place names used in the main text of this book and its maps compared with the spellings Wilson used for the same places. Occasionally the difference between the names given in Wilson's writings and those used today is more than a difference in spelling, however (the place Wilson knew as Tatien-lu is now known as Kangding, for example), and these equivalents are also included in this list. Unfortunately it has not been possible to ascertain the pinyin spelling for some of the smaller places mentioned in the story. These are shown in the text as Wilson spelt them, with the words 'called by Wilson', or 'known as' preceding them.

Pinyin transliteration	Transliteration used by E H Wilson
Anhui	Anhwei
An Xian	An Hsien
Badong	Patung
Baoxing	Mupin
Changyang	Chang Yang
Chengdu	Chengtu
Chongqing	Chung-King
Dadu River	Tatu River, Tung River
Danba	Romi Chango
Daning	Taning
Daning River	Taning River
Emei Shan	Mount Omei
Fang Xian	Fang Hsien
Fujian	Fukien
Fulin	Hanyuan
Guan Xian	Kuan Hsien
Guizhou	Kweichow
Hankou	Hankow
Henan	Honan
Hongya	Hungya hsien
Hubei	Hupeh
Hunan	no change

Jiangsu	Kiangsu
Jiangxi	Kiangsi
Jilin	Kirin
Jiujiang	Kiu Kiang
Kangding	Tatien-lu, Tachien-lu
Kunming	Yunnan Fu
Leshan	Kiating
Langzhong	Paoning
Lushan hills	no change
Manhao	no change
Mengzi	Mengtsze
Min River	no change
Nanjing	Nanking
Pingshan	Ping-Shan-Pa
Pingwu	Lungan Fu
Pu'er	Puerh
Shaanxi	Shensi
Shandong	Shantung
Shanghai	no change
Shanxi	Shansi
Sichuan	Szechuan
Simao	Szemao
Songpan	Sungpan
Wushan	no change
Xiangtan	Hsiang t'an
Xiaojin	MonKong Ting
Xingshan	Hsing Shan
Xuanhan	Tunghsiang
Ya'an	Ya-Chow
Yibin	Suifu
Yichang	Ichang
Yunnan	no change
Zheduo	Cheh-to
Zhushan	Ch'u shan

Maps

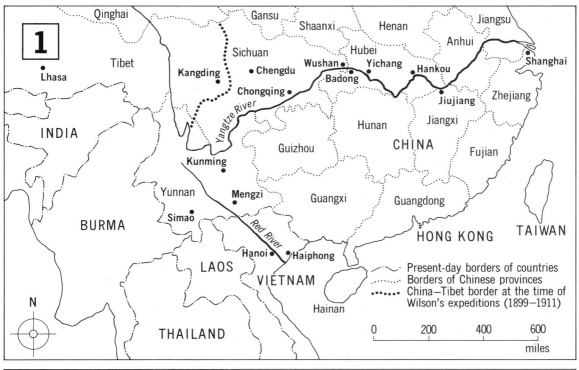

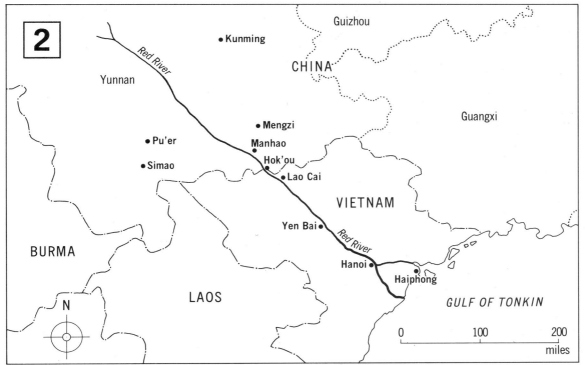

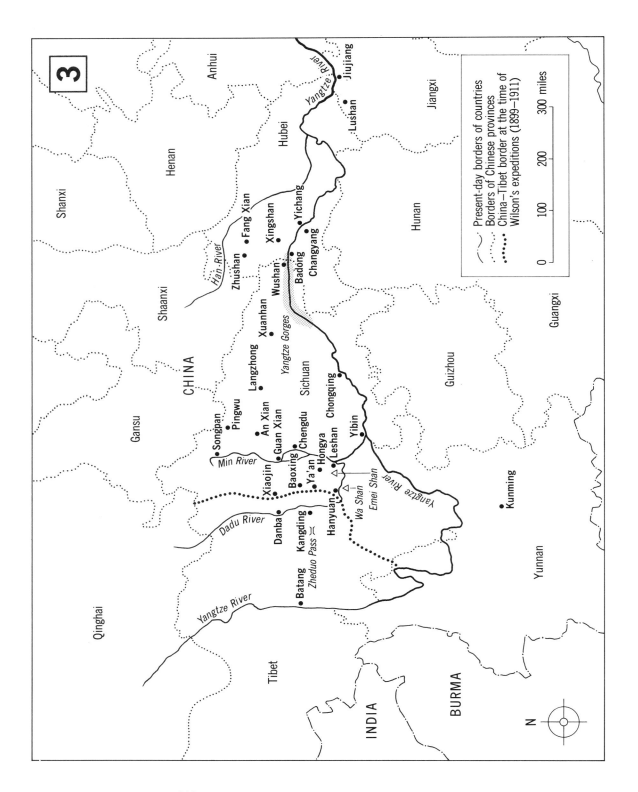

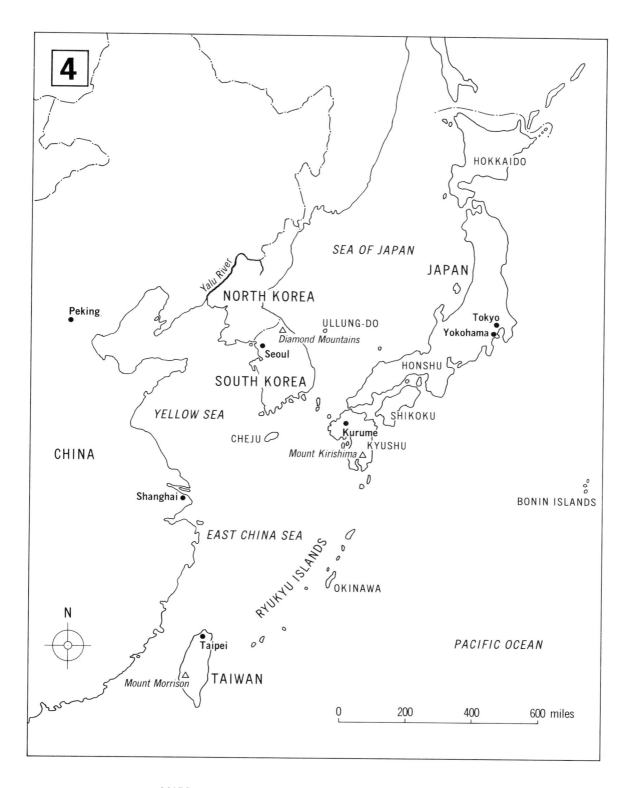

Index

Ernest Wilson is referred to as EW.

Veitch & Sons, 12–13, 24, 27, 43, 44
Veronica, 41
Viburnum, 130
    betulifolium, 130
    carlesii, 86
    cinnamonifolium, 130
    davidii, 130
    foetidum, 130
    hupehense, 130
    rhytidophyllum, 130
Victoria Falls, 106
Vilmorin, Maurice de, 25

Wa Shan, 32–3, 57
Wa-Wu, 57–8, 59
Wallis, E J, 46–7, 60
Ward, Frank Kingdon, 70
Williams, J C, 125, 128
Willmott, Ellen, 45, 47, 120
Wilson, Ellen ('Nellie')
    to Boston, 61
    death of, 114
    Ellen Willmott on, 45
    and EW, 4, 5, 14, 45, 60
    and EW's parents, 4, 63
    family home, 10
    funeral, 116
    in Japan, 80, 81, 84
    in Korea, 86, 91
    marriage, 25–6
Wilson, Ernest H
    and Arnold Arboretum, 5, 13, 46, 47, 60–62 *passim*, 77, 83, 94, 95–6, 110, 112
    background and youth, 3, 9–10, 12, 25
    character, 1–2, 7, 73, 78
    and Chinese employees, 5–6, 17, 19, 28, 51, 53, 57, 63, 75
    Chinese expeditions:
        for Arnold Arboretum, 45–60, 62–75
        for Veitch & Co, 12–25, 28–43
    'Chinese' Wilson epithet, 6, 77
    death, 114
    dogs, 22, 33, 35, 36, 56, 57, 72–3, 114

employment at Royal Botanic Gardens, Kew, 10, 45
equipment for expeditions, 19–22
and European botanical institutions, 60
Far Eastern expeditions:
    to China, 12–25, 28–43, 45–60, 62–75
    to Japan, 79–82, 84, 90–91
    to Korea, 86, 91
    to Taiwan, 88–90, 92–3
fascination with Far East, 6–7
First World War, 81–2, 83, 85–6
funeral, 116
honours and presentations, 24, 44, 78, 83, 114, 129
hunting trips in China, 48, 50–51
importance as plant collector, 117
leg injury, 73–5
monument, 116
move to the United States, 60–61
objects of expeditions, 13–14, 28, 46, 63, 82, 88, 95–6
photography, 46–7, 56, 61, 85, 91, 93, 96, 97, 99, 109–10
plant introductions, 117–30
plant materials collected, 7, 22, 24–5, 33, 38, 42, 43, 51, 60, 67, 72, 75, 76, 77, 82, 85, 91, 93, 94, 97, 102, 103, 117
public speaking, 94
publications:
    America's Greatest Garden, 109
    Aristocrats of the Garden, 13, 25, 110
    Aristocrats of the Trees, 9, 112
    articles for periodicals, 2, 40, 109
    Cherries of Japan, The, 83
    China, Mother of Gardens, 78, 112
    Conifers and Taxads of Japan, The, 83
    If I Were to Make a Garden, 109
    Lilies of Eastern Asia, The, 110
    More Aristocrats of the Garden, 112, 113